Grow-With-Me

Bible

Tree of Life Version

TLV

The Tree of Life Bible Society, founded in 2008, is a nonprofit ministry that has been commissioned by our greater community to produce and safeguard the creation of a brand new Biblical text of the Holy Scriptures: from Genesis - Revelation, entitled the Tree of Life Version. To learn more: Visit us at www.TLVBibleSociety.org. Donations towards providing free Tree of Life Holy Scriptures for global outreach and discipleship are received at:

TREE OF LIFE
BIBLE SOCIETY

P.O. BOX 221 | ROME, GA 30162 USA

Welcome to the TLV Grow-With-Me Bible!

This is an abridged edition of the TLV Holy Scriptures carefully selected for
all children to learn to read – with their parents and siblings together.

· ◆ · ◆ · ◆ ·

This is a collection of TLV Bible verses, story by story, for one full year!

The chapters start in Genesis and end in Revelation.

34 of the stories are from the ancient Jewish scrolls written long before Messiah arrived in Bethlehem.
The other 20 of the stories are about the life and times of Jesus, the Messiah, and His followers.
Every TLV Bible calls Jesus = *Yeshua*.

YESHUA is the English letters to help you pronounce the Hebrew word for JESUS.
The word *Yeshua* means "salvation." Savior is the noun for the 'one who saves.'

· ◆ · ◆ · ◆ ·

God, our Heavenly Father, is eternal, invisible, and indivisible.

God is always the primary agent propelling His story forward.

ELOHIM is the English letters to help you pronounce the Hebrew word for GOD
The word *Elohim* means "One God in His Fullness." God is singular and plural at the same time!

RUACH is the English letters to help you pronounce the Hebrew word for SPIRIT
The word *Ruach* means "Breath" or "Wind." The Spirit of God is a noun and a verb at the same time!

ADONAI is the capital English letters we offer to help you pronounce the Hebrew word for LORD
The word ADONAI is a substitute for the Holy Name of God we don't even pronounce fully out loud!

· ◆ · ◆ · ◆ ·

Our coloring pages can be taped together to form your own Art Scroll!

You can make your own, or work together as a family, or a Bible Study Group.

These 52 weekly coloring pages – plus a lesson for Passover and Tabernacles each – make a great
faith-building homeschool craft. *Please see our Art Scroll Tutorial on page 221.* With every story, you
can build your own faith traditions and recognize the 'Holy Moments' with God hidden inside your Bible.

"We Believe the Bible says the two most important commandments are:

1st LOVE GOD
and
2nd LOVE ONE ANOTHER

We believe that growing to know God's Love revolves securely between those two boundaries."

A quote by Daniah Greenberg, TLV Founder

Grow-With-Me Bible
Table of Contents

Our Chapter Introductions & Hebrew Glossary

BRIEF NOTES: This is the Parent/Teacher Guide to help you understand the meta-narrative of this collection of TLV Bible verses for youth. Please review this, and note the verses were prayerfully chosen – in order to prepare for questions that may come out in the telling. We are also giving insight into which Hebrew term is appearing inside each chapter. We hope this helps inspire further understanding of how God's Words grow with you along the way.

Rest assured, the two most important commandments are: 1st LOVE GOD and 2nd LOVE ONE ANOTHER. We believe that growing to know God revolves securely between those two boundaries.

Aside from these helps, the *Grow-With-Me Bible* is TLV Holy Scripture only and you can find the same verses noted that match your full *Tree of Life Family Bible*. Since every week includes one page of verses and one coloring page, you can look for more of the story inside the double spaces when you get older and want to know more details.

No.	Chapter Heading and Introductory Notes	New Hebrew Terms:
1	**God Breathes Life** God creates all the World, including male and female. God rests on the seventh day. God gives the breath of life to man, brings forth woman, and invites them to help make His Garden to grow.	*Ruach Elohim* – Spirit of God *Adonai Elohim* – LORD God
2	**God Covers Adam and Eve** The Garden has two trees in the middle. But, there was a lie hiding there! Where are the two people? And why are they hiding from God?	*cheruvim* – guardian angels
3	**God Warns their Son** The husband and wife have two children! Who is God speaking to in the Bible? What tragedy happens when people ignore God's words?	*Adonai* – The LORD
4	**God Saves a Family** When God wanted to save humanity, Noah was given a way to escape the chaos and built an ark. Noah listened to God's voice and saved all the animals. Then, God saved all Noah's seed, too!	
5	**God Humbles Rebellion** Humanity repopulated the earth! But, they lost their way again when they thought they could reach heaven by themselves! How did God stop their plan without flooding the earth again?	
6	**God Spoke to Abram** Abram listened to God and left his past behind. God promised to be with him, to give him many children and land far and wide. God blessed Abram and his wife and pledged again to give them a child of their own.	*El Shaddai* – Almighty God
7	**God Keeps His Promise** Abram is named Abraham, and Sarah gives birth to their son, Isaac! God's promise to them is now for Isaac too! Isaac marries Rebecca and they have twins! What a blessing! How can they learn to share in the promise?	*mitzvot* - commandments

8	**God Reunites Brothers** From Abraham to Isaac and then, Jacob, God's promise has endured. When Jacob fathers twelve sons with two wives and their two slaves, how can their family ever stay together? Doesn't peace begin at home?	
9	**God Rescues a Baby** In 400 years, Jacob's family grows to 600,000 people! Now they are stuck in Egypt as Pharaoh's slaves. Did God forget His promise? No! God hid a baby in Pharaoh's family! When God is ready, He makes a way to save!	*Bnei-Israel* – Children of Israel
10	**God Calls to Moses** God calls to Moses by His HOLY NAME! Moses heard His voice and TWO miraculous signs urging him back to Egypt to save the Children of Israel. ADONAI said He alone would be known as -the ONE- who set Israel free!	*Hineni* – 'Here I am!' *tza-ra'at* – leprosy disease
11	**God Challenges Pharaoh** Moses and his brother Aaron face Pharaoh to end their slavery. With great plagues, God judges idol worships in Egypt. God wants the Hebrews to celebrate His Passover. God sets them free with great miracles and wonders.	
12	**God Births a Nation** Pharaoh pursues the Children of Israel to take them captive again, but God gives Moses a new miracle! God parts the Sea of Reeds and the Israelites cross over on dry land through the night. But, how does God stop Pharaoh's army?	
13	**God Covenants with *B'nei-Yisrael*** God commands Moses to prepare the people to meet Him at Mount Sinai.God's thunderous voice speaks to them and they promise to follow His Words, again and again. God commands Moses to make a sacrifice and sprinkle them, to make them a holy nation of priests. The Scroll of the Covenant is our God's law.	*Torah* – 1st Five Biblical Books *Shabbat* – the 7th day, for rest *manna* – bread from Heaven *shofar* – ram's horn to blast
14	**God Teaches His People** God spoke the Ten Commandments, and His appointed yearly feasts, to them. Again, they agreed twice to follow God and made sacrifices to seal the Covenant Why did 70 Elders go with Moses and Aaron up the mountain? What happened?	*Yom Shabbat* – Sabbath Day *matzot* – matzahs
15	**God Visits His Tent** God created our world and made the 7th day for us to rest, safe and sound. God watches over us. God keeps meeting with Moses to give him instructions Moses asks God to stay with us forever. What does God want us to know about Him?	*Shabbatot* – Sabbaths *Shavuot* – Weeks
16	**God Disciplines the Scoffers** God commands Moses to send twelve princes of Israel to spy out the good land He promised to give to the seed of Abraham, Isaac, and Jacob. But, only Joshua and Caleb bring back good news! What did the others have to say?	*tzitzit* – fringes of holiness

17	**God Keeps Loving His People** Moses is God's scribe, the writer, of His Words to us! His last verses include the WATCHWORD of Israel that we say and we write on scrolls to remember to teach to our children. Go now! _Please under line: Deuteronomy 6:6-9_	_mitzvah_ – a good deed or righteous act
18	**God Answers their Shout** God wants to give them a city. Joshua is leading the people, now. How can they take a city? They are not warriors, they are wanderers! They left Egypt 40 years ago! How does He give them land? How does He teach them to trust Him?	_chazak_ – be strong and very courageous! _kohanim_ – ministering priests _shofarot_ – rams horns
19	**God Fights the Battle** God's laws that Moses wrote down are so important! God chose Deborah as a judge to help the people obey God's Words. When Barak was chosen to lead them into battle, why did he ask Deborah to go with him? How does God help?	
20	**God Grants her Prayers** Only God creates life! When a very sad wife went to the Temple to pray, the priest misunderstood! But, Hannah trusted God and kept believing! God gave them a son! Now her son, Samuel needs to pray, too? How do we hear God?	_ADONAI Tzva'ot_ – Lord of Hosts/Armies _kohen_ – priest _shalom_ – peace, greetings, fullness
21	**God Anoints a King** God chose a boy to be Israel's new king! When Goliath, a giant warrior, was bullying all Israel, David struck him down with a single stone. God was – WITH DAVID – when he killed Goliath. To be anointed is to be – with God! Are you?	_ADONAI Elohim Tzva'ot_ _The LORD God of Hosts_
22	**God Sends a Prophet** God appoints prophets to speak for Him! When God sent Elijah to bring down the pagan idol worshippers, the God of Israel showed up and defeated them! When God was ready to take Elijah up, who did He choose to use next?	_Avi_ – Dad
23	**God Helps Mothers** God uses Elisha to heal water, create oil, heal a child, multiply food, find an axe head, open visions of armies, and even his dead bones are miraculous! When God helps mothers, the children see, too! Have you ever seen God do a miracle?	
24	**God Proclaims His Promise** God is especially good at comforting us. Did you know that God tells His secrets to prophets, like Jeremiah? During the worst of times, even the Babylonian Exile, God declared SHALOM to His people - Israel! God can always renew hope!	
25	**God Corrects Bad Behavior** God sent Jonah to save a city! But, Jonah went elsewhere and God had to teach him a lesson – quick! Have you ever turned the wrong way and got lost? God rarely forces His will on us, but He sure knows how to point us back to His ways!	_Sheol_ – Hell

26	**God Tabernacles – With Us!** God tells generation after generation that He will stay close to the people that love Him. Every year, we are commanded to celebrate the fullness of our joy by thanking God with a feast! How do you celebrate God's love with your family?	*Ruach* – breath or wind *kedoshim* – holy ones *echad* – one (plural) *Sukkot* – Tabernacles
27	**God is Our LORD** Psalm 1 can teach you to love God's Words. Psalm 19 can teach you to love His Creation. Psalm 23 can teach you how to find peace with God. Psalms are songs that are great for teaching you to pray. Try saying one out loud, then you pray!	
28	**God is Our Strength** Psalm 67 can help you proclaim God's love to the world. Psalm 84 can help you find the way to God's House. Psalm 91 can help you feel safe and secure in God's love. Psalms are great for listening for God! Read one and wait for Him.	*selah* – pause *Elyon* – God Most High
29	**God is Our Song** Psalm 100 is a song of thanksgiving to God. Psalm 111 is a song of praise for Who He is! Psalm 133 is a song that invites God's blessing to come upon us! Psalm 150 is a song about instruments! Make music and sing praises to God!	*Halleluyah* – Praise God!
30	**God Lets Us Choose** God gives us wisdom every day in the Proverbs. Here are seven days of verses from the Proverbs to start with. Can you read just a few verses a day for seven days? If we all read together, we can help each other trust God even more!	
31	**God Hears her Heart** God responds to people who ache for His love on the earth. When a widow lost both her sons, only one of their wives begged to return with her to God. God blessed their return with a kinsman-redeemer! Is anything too hard for God?	
32	**God Appoints her Steps** God know exactly how to rescue His people! God hid an orphaned woman in the courts of a pagan king. At just the right time, God's favor on Esther exposed the threat and saved her people! Will you be ready when God chooses you?	
33	**God Protects the Scribe** God was watching Daniel and speaking His secrets about Messiah's return someday. But Daniel was a slave for a pagan king. When Daniel refused to bow down to anyone but the God of Israel, how would God's Words be saved for us?	
34	**God Builds His House** God moved on the heart of the Persian King and he sent forth an edict. He would let Ezra and Nehemiah go home to their land and build God's House. Did you know that they found the Torah Scroll and celebrated Tabernacles? WOW!	

35	**God Ḥides the Savior** Another 400 years later, with Israel under Roman rule, babies are in danger again like at the time of Moses! So God created a BABY BOY – by the power of His Holy Spirit – inside a virgin, named Miriam. Joseph married her and the Baby was born in a manger in Bethlehem! They ran away to Egypt, then… on the eighth day, the Baby was circumcised and later arrived at the Temple! What? Didn't anybody know how special this Baby was? Read the verses about what the Temple witnesses said about him… Every child is a gift from God. No one knows who you will become except God! Do you think perhaps God hides His Spirit inside us to be His witnesses, too?	*Yeshua ha-Mashiach* – Jesus the Messiah *Ben-David* – Son of David *Ben-Avraham* – Son of Abraham *brit-milah* – circumcision *Ruach ha-Kodesh* – Holy Spirit *bracha* – blessing *Natzaret* – Nazareth *Natzerati* – Nazarene
36	**God Speaks Through His Son** God sends His Son, Yeshua, to speak His Torah – even inside the Temple! What could a boy say that could make even the adults listen? Was the boy making up the words Himself? No! Yeshua was speaking His Father's Words – can you?	
37	**God Arrives!** God is speaking from Heaven? What is He saying? What is Yeshua doing? And where did the dove come from? This is the most amazing picture of when God the Father, Yeshua the Son and the Holy Spirit are all together as One! Wow!	*Ben-Elohim* – Son of God
38	**God Leads Followers** God sent Yeshua to find students to teach. Students become disciples when they learn to follow and obey. When we get closer to God we become more like His children: loving, kind, patient. What are you learning from your teachers?	*Ruach Adonai* – Spirit of the LORD *Kinneret* – the Sea of Galilee
39	**God Invites Little Children** God loves to bless us. Yeshua tells us to remain like little children – to stay protected and safe in God's love. When adults overlook little children, they can grow up lonely or afraid. Trust in God! Even babies can feel at peace – with God.	
40	**God is Our Father** God sent His Son to feed the people with God's Words, and bread, too! When Yeshua was asked how to pray, He said, "Our Father in Heaven…" Do you know those words – the Lord's Prayer? That is the most famous prayer in the Bible!	
41	**God Blesses *Yeshua*** God sent Yeshua to Jerusalem to celebrate the Passover. They shouted at the entrance – blessing the arrival of people coming with their Passover lambs. Do you think they knew He was the Messiah? Oh, how they shouted, "Please save!"	'*Baruch haba b'shem Adonai*' – 'Blessed is He who comes in the Name of the Lord.' *Hoshia-na* – please save!
42	**God Remembers the Passover** Every Passover we remember our freedom from slavery. Messiah Yeshua ate Seder dinner with His disciples. Though Messiah let Judah go to betray Him and warned Peter would deny Him. Messiah Yeshua gave them all a new command: "Just as I have loved you, so you must also love one another…" *(Read the rest!)*	*Kohen Hagadol* – High Priest *matzah* – unleavened bread *seder* – in order *Hallel* – Praise

43	**God Chooses the Scapegoat** God's Passover Seder night was not over! Yeshua prays to His Father and Judah signals for His arrest. Peter denies Him, and the trial before the Jewish leaders begins at dawn. Before the Roman Governor, who does the crowd set free?	*Abba* – Father *Bar-abba* –Barabbas (son of the father)
44	**God Provides the Lamb** From that trial to the execution, Messiah Yeshua never answered His accusers. When He gave up His Spirit the Temple curtain split in two and the Holy Place opened! They buried Him in a sealed tomb. How dare they crucify the Messiah?	*Yeshua Ha-Nazrati* – Jesus of Nazareth
45	**God Saves the World** God raised Messiah Yeshua from the dead! God's promise to forgive sin and defeat death is ours now! For God so loved the world that He gave His One and Only Son, that whoever believes in Him shall not perish but have eternal life.	*Shalom alechim* – peace to you
46	**God Forgives Unbelief** Imagine the excitement of God's salvation appearing on earth! But Thomas needed to see for Himself! Can you believe without seeing Him? The disciples saw even more miracles! Now they are sure He is God! But, what about Peter?	*Maschiach Ben-Elohim* – Messiah Son of God
47	**God Lifts *Yeshua* Up** God spoke through the prophet Isaiah about the coming Messiah who would suffer. Messiah Yeshua stayed for 40 days and appeared to over 500 witnesses! Then, Yeshua was lifted up into heaven to sit at His Father's right hand.	
48	**God Gives His Spirit** On the Feast of Weeks, 50 days after the Last Seder, the disciples are gathered at the Temple for the promise from Yeshua to arrive. God rewards their prayers with the gift of His Holy Spirit. The Comforter is here to reunite His followers.	
49	**God Opens Blind Eyes** God is after Saul's heart. Saul has been persecuting Yeshua's followers. Yeshua speaks directly to Saul and he is struck blind! Paul repents and recovers, but what a surprise to the religious leaders in Jerusalem. Who is this new person?	
50	**God Frees the Captives** God is using this new Paul to stir up people with the Good News of Messiah's Resurrection. Miracles were happening and many were being saved – even a fortune teller was delivered from demons! How did that land Paul in a jail cell?	*Bar Yeshua* – Son of Salvation *El-Elyon* – God, Most High God
51	**God is Our Salvation** God had Paul write a letter to the Romans to explain that Yeshua is salvation for all people. First, He came for the Jews who have been following God for thousands of years. AND, Yeshua came for all nations to join in the celebration of eternal freedom in Messiah for all mankind.	

52	**God Heals Our Family Tree** When we let God be our Heavenly Father, we each become His own. The Spirit of adoption is for all of us to rest assured that we are uniquely loved. When God helps us to love one another, He heals our hearts and rebuilds our family tree.	
53	**God Creates His Kingdom** God builds each one up into a mature and loving person who knows right from wrong and seeks to follow Him with all their heart. Fitted together like living stones, our fellowship builds us up into the Temple of Our God - alive on earth!	
54	**God Lights the Way Home** When heaven meets earth and Messiah returns for His People, God's Kingdom will light the way home for all His children. No more tears or sorrow – only love and joy and peace forevermore. Shalom, shalom Jerusalem. Amen and amen.	*ADONAI Elohei-Tz'va'ot* – The LORD God of Hosts

TLV Abridged Glossary

Abba - Father

ADONAI – יהוה YHVH, The LORD

ADONAI *Echad* – The LORD is One

ADONAI *Elohim* – The LORD God*963

ADONAI *Eloheinu* – The LORD our God

ADONAI *Elyon* – The LORD God Most High

ADONAI *Nissi* – The LORD our Banner

ADONAI *Tzva'ot* – The LORD of Hosts

ADONAI *Elohei-Tzva'ot* - The LORD God of Hosts

ADONAI *Ro-eh* – The LORD our Shepherd

aliyah – to ascend

amen – let it be so

Avi – Dad

avodah – service to God

Bar-Abba – Barabbas, son of the father

Bar Mitzvah – son of the commandment

Baruch haba – blessed is he who comes/87

basar echad – one flesh

Ben-Adam –Son of Adam

Ben-David –Son of David

Ben-Elohim – Son of God

Ben-Elyon – Son of the Most High

beelzebub – lord of flies

Besorah – Good News

Bnei-Yisrael – The Childen of Israel

bracha - blessings

Brit Chadashah – New Covenant

brit-milah – circumcision

chazak – be strong

cheruv/cheruvim – glory beings

chesed - mercy, kindness

El – God

El Elyon – God, God Most High

El Shaddai – God Almighty

Elyon – God Most High

emunah – faith (verb)

Gan Eden – Garden of Eden

Gehenna - hell

gerim – convert to Judaism

goel - close kinsman - redeemer

Hallel - Praise

Halleluyah – Praise God

hametz - leaven

Hanukkah – Feast of Dedication

HaShem – The Name, unspoken

hineni – "Here I am" answering a call

hoshia-na – Please save!

kadosh - Holy

kedoshim – saints

Ketuvim – The Writings

Kriot – Judah's home town

Kohen/kohanim – priest(s)

kohen gadol – high priest

korban - dedicated sacrifice

lashon ha-ra – evil speech

magen – shield

magilla – 5 Books (Songs, Ruth, Lamentations, Ecclesiastes & Esther)

manna – bread from heaven

Mashiach – Messiah, anointed one

matzah/matzot – unleavened bread(s)

midrash – teaching

mishkan – tent

moed/moadim – appointed time(s)

menorah/menorot – lampstand(s)

mezuzah/mezuzot - doorpost(s)

mikveh – ritual immersion pool

mitzvah/mitzvot - commandment(s)

Natzaret/Natzrati – Nazarene, branch

Nevi'im – The Prophets

niddah – unclean

olam ha-ba – the world to come

olam ha-zeh – this world

Oy – Woe!

Parashat – a *Shabbat* reading section

Parsha – a *Shabbat* reading section

Pesach - Passover

rabbi - teacher

Rosh Chodesh – New Moon, Head of the Month

Rosh Hashana – Head of the Year

Ruach – Spirit, breath of God

Ruach Elohim – Spirit of God

Ruach ha-Kodesh – The Holy Spirit

satan – adversary, accuser, Satan

seder - order

selah – a pause

Shabbat/Shabbatot– Sabbath rest

Shaddai – All Sufficient One

shaliach/shlichim - apostle(s), the sent one(s), emissaries

shalom - peace

shalom aleichem – peace to you

shammash – servant leaders

Shavuot – Feast of Weeks, Pentecost

Shema – Hear, listen

Shema Yisrael! – Hear O Israel!

Shemini atzeret – the last day of the Feast

shekel – currency

Sheol - hell

shiva - mourning

shofar – ram's horn

sukkah - booth

Sukkot - booths, Feast of Tabernacles

TANAKH – acronym for the three sections: Torah, Neviim & Ketuvim

talmidim – students

tefillin – phylacteries for prayer

teshuvah – to turn back toward

tevilah – high praise to God

tikvah – hope

todah – thanksgiving

Torah – the Law

tza-ra'at - leprosy

tzedakah – alms for the poor

tzedakim – righteous ones

tzitzit – fringes on garment

Yeshua – Jesus, salvation

Yom Kippur – Day of Atonement

Yom Shabbat – Day of the *Sabbath*

zaken/zakenim – elder(s)

This Bible Belongs To:

Zaiden

From:

Grandpa LeRoy   Grandma Cheryl

On This Day:

1. God Breathes Life

In the beginning God created the heavens and the earth. Now the earth was chaos and waste, darkness was on the surface of the deep, and the *Ruach Elohim* was hovering upon the surface of the water.

Then God said, "Let there be light!" and there was light. God saw that the light was good. So God distinguished the light from the darkness. God called the light "day," and the darkness He called "night." So there was evening and there was morning—one day.

Then God said, "Let there be an expanse in the midst of the water! Let it be for separating water from water." So God made the expanse and it separated the water that was below the expanse from the water that was over the expanse. And it happened so. God called the expanse "sky."

So there was evening and there was morning—a second day.

Then God said, "Let the water below the sky be gathered to one place. Let the dry ground appear." And it happened so. God called the dry ground "land," and the collection of the water He called "seas." And God saw that it was good.

Then God said, "Let the land sprout grass, green plants yielding seed, fruit trees making fruit, each according to its species with seed in it, upon the land." And it happened so.

Genesis 1:11

So there was evening and there was morning—a third day.

Then God said, "Let lights in the expanse of the sky be for separating the day from the night. They will be for signs and for seasons and for days and years. They will be for lights in the expanse of the sky to shine upon the land." And it happened so.

Then God made the two great lights—the greater light for dominion over the day, and the lesser light as well as the stars for dominion over the night.

God set them in the expanse of the sky to shine on the land and to have dominion over the day and over the night and to separate the light from the darkness.

And God saw that it was good.

So there was evening and there was morning—a fourth day.

Then God said, "Let the waters swarm with swarms of living creatures! Let flying creatures fly above the land across the expanse of the sky."

Genesis 1:13-20

Then God blessed them by saying, "Be fruitful and multiply and fill the water in the seas. Let the flying creatures multiply on the land."

So there was evening and there was morning—a fifth day.

Then God said, "Let the land bring forth living creatures according to their species — livestock, crawling creatures and wild animals, according to their species." And it happened so.

Genesis 1:22-24

Then God said, "Let Us make man in Our image, after Our likeness! Let them rule over the fish of the sea, over the flying creatures of the sky, over the livestock, over the whole earth, and over every crawling creature that crawls on the land."

God created humankind in His image, in the image of God He created him, male and female He created them.

God blessed them and God said to them, "Be fruitful and multiply, fill the land, and conquer it. Rule over the fish of the sea, the flying creatures of the sky, and over every animal that crawls on the land."

Then God said, "I have just given you every green plant yielding seed that is on the surface of the whole land, and every tree, which has the fruit of a tree yielding seed. They are to be food for you. Also for every wild animal, every flying creature of the sky and every creature that crawls on the land which has life, every green plant is to be food." And it happened so. So God saw everything that He made, and behold it was very good.

So there was evening and there was morning—the sixth day.

Genesis 1:26-31

So the heavens and the earth were completed along with their entire array. God completed – on the seventh day – His work that He made, and He ceased – on the seventh day – from all His work that He made.

Then God blessed the seventh day and sanctified it, for on it He ceased from all His work that God created for the purpose of preparing.

Genesis 2:1-3

Then ADONAI Elohim formed the man out of the dust from the ground and He breathed into his nostrils a breath of life – so the man became a living being. Then ADONAI Elohim planted a garden in Eden in the east, and there He put the man whom He had formed.

Then ADONAI Elohim caused to sprout from the ground every tree that was desirable to look at and good for food. Now the Tree of Life was in the middle of the garden, and also the Tree of Knowledge of Good and Evil.

Genesis 2:7-9

Then ADONAI Elohim took the man and gave him rest in the Garden of Eden in order to cultivate and watch over it. Then ADONAI Elohim commanded the man saying, "From all the trees of the garden you are most welcome to eat. But of the Tree of the Knowledge of Good and Evil you must not eat. For when you eat from it, you most assuredly will die!"

Then ADONAI Elohim said, "It is not good for the man to be alone. Let Me make a well-matched helper for him."

Genesis 2:15-18

ADONAI Elohim caused a deep sleep to fall on the man and he slept; and He took one of his ribs and closed up the flesh in its place. ADONAI Elohim built the rib, which He had taken from the man, into a woman. Then He brought her to the man. Then the man said, "This one, at last, is bone of my bones and flesh from my flesh. This one is called woman, for from man was taken this one."

Genesis 2:21-23

So the heavens and the earth were completed along with their entire array. God completed – on the seventh day – His work that He made, and He ceased – on the seventh day – from all His work that He made.

From Genesis 2:1 TLV ©2018, image #1/54

2. God Covers Adam and Eve

But the serpent was shrewder than any animal of the field that ADONAI Elohim made. So it said to the woman, "Did God really say, 'You must not eat from all the trees of the garden'?"

The woman said to the serpent, "Of the fruit of the trees, we may eat. But of the fruit of the tree which is in the middle of the garden, God said, 'You must not eat of it and you must not touch it, or you will die.'"

The serpent said to the woman, "You most assuredly won't die! For God knows that when you eat of it, your eyes will be opened and you will be like God, knowing good and evil."

Now the woman saw that the tree was good for food, and that it was a thing of lust for the eyes, and that the tree was desirable for imparting wisdom. So she took of its fruit and she ate. She also gave to her husband who was with her and he ate.

Then the eyes of both of them were opened and they knew that they were naked; so they sewed fig leaves together and made for themselves loin-coverings.

And they heard the sound of ADONAI Elohim going to and fro in the garden in the wind of the day. So the man and his wife hid themselves from the presence of ADONAI Elohim in the midst of the Tree of the garden.

Then ADONAI Elohim called to the man and He said to him, "Where are you?"

Then he said, "Your sound—I heard it in the garden and I was afraid. Because I am naked, I hid myself."

Then He said, "Who told you that you are naked? Have you eaten from the Tree from which I commanded you not to eat?"

Then the man said, "The woman whom You gave to be with me—she gave me of the Tree, and I ate."

ADONAI Elohim said to the woman, "What did you do?"

The woman said, "The serpent deceived me and I ate."

ADONAI Elohim said to the serpent,

"Cursed are you above all the livestock
 and above every animal of the field.

On your belly will you go,
 and dust will you eat
   all the days of your life.

I will put animosity
 between you and the woman—
   between your seed and her seed.

He will crush your head,
 and you will crush his heel.

To the woman He said,

"I will greatly increase your pain from
    conception to labor.
  In pain will you give birth to children.
  Your desire will be toward your husband,
    yet he must rule over you."

    Then to the man He said, "Because you
listened to your wife's voice and ate of the tree
which I commanded you, saying, 'You must not
eat of it':

  Cursed is the ground because of you—
  with pain will you eat of it
    all the days of your life.

Thorns and thistles will sprout for you.
  You will eat the plants of the field,
By the sweat of your brow will you eat food,
  until you return to the ground,
    since from it were you taken.

  For you are dust,
    and to dust will you return."

    Now Adam named his wife Eve because
she was the mother of all the living.

ADONAI Elohim made Adam and his wife
tunics of skin and He clothed them.

    Then *ADONAI Elohim* said, "Behold, the
man has become like one of Us, knowing good
and evil. So now, in case he stretches out his
hand and takes also from the Tree of Life and
eats and lives forever,"
    ADONAI Elohim sent him away from the
Garden of Eden, to work the ground from which
he had been taken.

    And He expelled the man; and at the
east of the Garden of Eden He had *cheruvim*
dwell along, with the whirling sword of flame,
to guard the way to the Tree of Life.

Genesis 3:1-24

ADONAI Elohim made Adam and his wife tunics of skin and He clothed them. Then ADONAI Elohim said, "Behold, the man has become like one of Us, knowing good and evil. So now, in case he stretches out his hand and takes also from the Tree of Life and eats and lives forever,"

From Genesis 3:21-22 TLV ©2018, image #2/54

3. God Warns their Son

Now the man had relations with Eve his wife and she became pregnant and gave birth to Cain. She said, "I produced a man with ADONAI." Then she gave birth again, to his brother Abel.

Abel became a shepherd of flocks while Cain became a worker of the ground. So it happened after some time that Cain brought an offering of the fruit of the ground to ADONAI, while Abel—he also brought of the firstborn of his flock and their fat portions.

Now ADONAI looked favorably upon Abel and his offering, but upon Cain and his offering He did not look favorably. Cain became very angry, and his countenance fell.

Then ADONAI said to Cain, "Why are you angry? And why has your countenance fallen? If you do well, it will lift. But if you do not do well, sin is crouching at the doorway. Its desire is for you, but you must master it."

Cain spoke to Abel his brother. While they were in the field, Cain rose up against Abel his brother and killed him.

Then ADONAI said to Cain, "Where is Abel, your brother?"

"I don't know," he said. "Am I my brother's keeper?"

Then He said, "What have you done? The voice of your brother's blood is crying out to Me from the ground. So now, cursed are you from the ground which opened its mouth to receive your brother's blood from your hand. As often as you work the ground, it will not yield its crops to you again. You will be a restless wanderer on the earth."

Cain said to ADONAI, "My iniquity is too great to bear! Since You expelled me today from the face of the ground and I must be hidden from Your presence, then I will be a restless wanderer on the earth—anyone who finds me will kill me!"

But ADONAI said to him, "In that case, anyone who kills Cain is to be avenged seven times over."

So ADONAI put a mark on Cain, so that anyone who found him would not strike him down. Then Cain left ADONAI's presence and dwelled in the Land of Wandering, east of Eden.

Genesis 4:1-16

Adam was intimate with his wife again, and she gave birth to a son and she named him Seth, "For God has appointed me another seed in place of Abel — since Cain killed him," To Seth, also was born a son. He named him Enosh.

Then people began to call on ADONAI's Name.

Genesis 4:25-26

When God created Adam, in the likeness of God He made him. Male and female He created them, and He blessed them and called their name "Adam" when He created them.

Adam lived 130 years, then fathered a son in his likeness, after his image, and named him Seth. Then the days of Adam after he fathered Seth were 800 years, and He fathered other sons and daughters. So all Adam's days that he lived were 930 years, and then he died.

Seth lived 105 years, then fathered Enosh. Seth lived 807 years after he fathered Enosh, and he fathered sons and daughters. So all Seth's days were 912 years, and then he died.

Enosh lived 90 years, then fathered Kenan. Enosh lived 815 years after he fathered Kenan, and he fathered sons and daughters. So all of Enosh's days were 905 years, and then he died.

Kenan lived 70 years, then fathered Mahalalel. Kenan lived 840 years after he fathered Mahalalel, he fathered sons and daughters. So all of Kenan's days were 910 years, and then he died.

Mahalalel lived 65 years, then fathered Jared. Mahalalel lived 830 years after he fathered Jared, and he fathered sons and daughters. So all of Mahalalel's days were 895 years, and then he died.

Jared lived 162 years, then fathered Enoch. Jared lived 800 years after he fathered Enoch, and he fathered sons and daughters. So all of Jared's days were 962 years, and then he died.

Enoch lived 65 years, then fathered Methuselah.

Now Enoch walked with God continually for 300 years after he fathered Methuselah, and he fathered sons and daughters. So all of Enoch's days were 365 years.
And Enoch continually walked with God—then he was not there, because God took him.

Methuselah lived 187 years and fathered Lamech. And Methuselah lived 782 years after he fathered Lamech, and he fathered other sons and daughters. So all of Methuselah's days were 969 years, and then he died.

Lamech lived 182 years and he fathered a son. And he named him Noah saying, "This one will comfort us from our work and from the pain of our hands because of the ground which ADONAI cursed."

Lamech lived 595 years after he fathered Noah, and he fathered sons and daughters. So all of Lamech's days were 777 years, and then he died. And Noah was 500 years old when he fathered Shem, Ham and Japheth.

Genesis 5:1b-31

Now the man had relations with Eve his wife and she became pregnant and gave birth to Cain. She said, "I produced a man with Adonai." Then she gave birth again, to his brother Abel.

From Genesis 4:1-2 TLV ©2018, image #3/54

15

4. God Saves a Family

Then *Adonai* saw that the wickedness of humankind was great on the earth, and that every inclination of the thoughts of their heart was only evil all the time.

So *Adonai* regretted that He made humankind on the earth, and His heart was deeply pained.

So *Adonai* said, "I will wipe out humankind, whom I have created, from the face of the ground, from humankind to livestock, crawling things and the flying creatures of the sky, because I regret that I made them." But Noah found favor in *Adonai*'s eyes.

These are the genealogies of Noah. Noah was a righteous man. He was blameless among his generation.

Noah continually walked with God. Noah fathered three sons: Shem, Ham and Japheth.

Now the earth was ruined before God, and the earth was filled with violence. God saw the earth, and behold it was ruined because all flesh had corrupted their way upon the earth.

Then God said to Noah, "The end of all flesh is coming before Me, for the earth is filled with violence because of them. Behold, I am about to bring ruin upon them along with the land. Make for yourself an ark of gopher wood."

Genesis 6:5-14a

So Noah did according to all that God commanded him; he did so exactly.

Genesis 6:22

Then *Adonai* said to Noah, "Come—you and all your household—into the ark. For you only do I perceive as righteous before Me in this generation.

Of every clean animal you shall take with you seven of each kind, male and female; and of the animals which themselves are not clean two, male and female; also of the flying creatures of the sky seven of every kind, male and female, to keep offspring alive on the face of the whole land. For in seven more days, I am going to make it rain upon the land forty days and forty nights, and I will wipe out all existence that I made from the face of the ground."

So Noah did all just as *Adonai* commanded him. Now Noah was 600 years old when the flood came – water upon the land.

Genesis 7:1-6

The flood was forty days upon the land, and the waters increased and lifted the ark, so that it rose above the land.

Genesis 7:17

The waters overpowered the land for 150 days.

Genesis 7:24

Then God remembered Noah and all the wild animals and all the livestock that were with him in the ark. So God caused a wind to pass over the land and the water subsided.

Genesis 8:1

It was in his six-hundred and first year – in the first month, on the first day of the month – that the waters had dried up from the land.

Then Noah removed the cover of the ark and he looked, and behold, the surface of the ground had dried up.

By the second month, on the twenty-seventh day of the month, the land was dry.

Genesis 8:13-14

Then God spoke to Noah, saying, "Come out of the ark, you and your wife, your sons and your sons' wives with you. Every animal that is with you of all flesh, including the flying creatures, livestock and every crawling creature that crawls on the land, bring out with you, and let them swarm in the land and be fruitful and multiply upon the land."

So Noah came out, with his sons, his wife, and his sons' wives. Every animal—every crawling creature, every flying creature, everything that crawls upon the land—came out from the ark in their families.

Then Noah built an altar to ADONAI and he took of every clean domestic animal and of every clean flying creature and he offered burnt offerings on the altar.

When ADONAI smelled the soothing aroma, ADONAI said in His heart, "I will never again curse the ground on account of man, even though the inclination of the heart of humankind is evil from youth. Nor will I ever again smite all living creatures, as I have done.

While all the days of the land remain, seedtime and harvest, cold and heat, summer and winter, day and night will not cease."

Genesis 8:15-22

God blessed Noah and his sons, and He said to them, "Be fruitful and multiply and fill the land. The fear and terror of you will be on every wild animal, and on every flying creature of the sky, with everything that crawls on the ground and with all the fish of the sea—into your hand they are given. Every crawling thing that is alive will be food for you, as are the green plants—I have now given you everything.

Only flesh with its life—that is, its blood—you must not eat!

Genesis 9:1-4

But as for you, be fruitful and multiply! Flourish in the land and multiply in it!"

Then God said to Noah and to his sons with him, saying, "Now I, behold, I am about to establish My covenant with you, and with your seed after you, and with every living creature that is with you, including the flying creatures, the livestock, and every wild animal with you, of all that is coming out of the ark—every animal of the earth. I will confirm My covenant with you—never again will all flesh be cut off by the waters of the flood, and never again will there be a flood to ruin the land."

Then God said, "This is the sign of the covenant that I am making between Me and you, and every living creature that is with you for all future generations. My rainbow do I place in the cloud, and it will be a sign of the covenant between Me and the land. ..."

Genesis 9:7-13

Then Noah built an altar to A*DONAI* and he took of every clean domestic animal and of every clean flying creature and he offered burnt offerings on the altar. When A*DONAI* smelled the soothing aroma, A*DONAI* said in His heart, "I will never again curse the ground on account of man, even though the inclination of the heart of humankind is evil from youth.
from Genesis 8:20-21 TLV ©2018, image #4/54

5. God Humbles Rebellion

Noah's sons who came out from the ark were Shem, Ham and Japheth, and Ham was the father of Canaan. These three were Noah's sons, and from these the whole earth dispersed.

Genesis 9:18-19

Now Noah lived 350 years after the flood. So all Noah's days were 950 years. Then he died.

Genesis 9:28-29

And these are the genealogical records of Noah's sons, Shem, Ham, and Japheth. Sons were born to them after the flood. Japheth's sons were Gomer, Magog, Madai, Javan, Tubal, Meshech and Tiras.

Genesis 10:1-2

Ham's sons were Cush, Mizraim, Put and Canaan.

Genesis 10:6

Shem's sons were Elam, Asshur, Arpachshad, Lud and Aram.

Genesis 10:22

Now the entire earth had the same language with the same vocabulary. When they traveled eastward, they found a valley-plain in the land of Shinar and settled there. They said to one another, "Come! Let's make bricks and bake them until they're hard." So they used bricks for stone, and tar for mortar.

Then they said, "Come! Let's build ourselves a city, with a tower whose top reaches into heaven. So let's make a name for ourselves, or else we will be scattered over the face of the whole land."

Then ADONAI came down to see the city and the tower that the sons of man had built.

ADONAI said, "Look, the people are one and all of them have the same language. So this is what they have begun to do. Now, nothing they plan to do will be impossible. Come! Let Us go down and confuse their language there, so that they will not understand each other's language."

So ADONAI scattered them from there over the face of the entire land, and they stopped building the city. This is why it is named Babel, because ADONAI confused the languages of the entire world there, and from there ADONAI scattered them over the face of the entire world.

These are the genealogical records of Shem: Shem was 100 years old when he fathered Arpachshad—two years after the flood. Shem lived 500 years after he fathered Arpachshad, and he fathered sons and daughters.

Arpachshad lived 35 years when he fathered Shelah. Arpachshad lived 403 years after he fathered Shelah, and fathered sons and daughters.

Shelah lived 30 years and he fathered Eber. Shelah lived 403 years after he fathered Eber, and fathered sons and daughters.

Eber lived 34 years and he fathered Peleg. Eber lived 430 years after he fathered Peleg, and he fathered sons and daughters.

Peleg lived 30 years and he fathered Reu. Peleg lived 209 years after he fathered Reu, and he fathered sons and daughters.

Reu lived 32 years and he fathered Serug. Reu lived 207 years after he fathered Serug, and he fathered sons and daughters.

Serug lived 30 years and fathered Nahor. Serug lived 200 years after he fathered Nahor, and he fathered sons and daughters.

Nahor lived 27 years and he fathered Terah. Nahor lived 119 years after he fathered Terah, and he fathered sons and daughters.

Terah lived 70 years when he fathered Abram, Nahor and Haran.

These are Terah's genealogies: Terah fathered Abram, Nahor and Haran.

Haran fathered Lot. Haran died before Terah his father, in the land of his birth, in Ur of the Chaldeans.

Abram and Nahor took wives for themselves. The name of Abram's wife was Sarai, and the name of Nahor's wife was Milcah—the daughter of Haran, father of Milcah and Iscah.

Sarai was barren; she did not have a child.

Terah took Abram his son and Lot, Haran's son, his grandson, and Sarai his daughter-in-law, his son Abram's wife, and he took them out of Ur of the Chaldeans to go to the land of Canaan.

But when they came to Haran, they settled there. Terah's days were 205 years, and Terah died in Haran.

Genesis 11

So **ADONAI** scattered them from there over the face of the entire land, and they stopped building the city. This is why it is named Babel, because **ADONAI** confused the languages of the entire world there, and from there **ADONAI** scattered them over the face of the entire world.

From Genesis 11:8-9 TLV ©2018, image #5/54

6. God Spoke to Abram

Then *Adonai* said to Abram,

"Get going out from your land,
and from your relatives,
and from your father's house,
to the land that I will show you

My heart's desire is to make you
into a great nation, to bless you,
to make your name great
so that you may be a blessing.

My desire is to bless those who bless you,
but whoever curses you I will curse,
and in you all the families of the earth
will be blessed.

So Abram went, just as *Adonai* had spoken to him. Also Lot went with him. (Now Abram was 75 years old when he departed from Haran.) Abram took Sarai his wife, and Lot his nephew, and all their possessions that they had acquired, and the people that they acquired in Haran, and they left to go to the land of Canaan, and they entered the land of Canaan.

Abram passed through the land as far as the place of Shechem, as far as Moreh's big tree. (The Canaanites were in the land then.) Then *Adonai* appeared to Abram, and said, "I will give this land to your seed." So there he built an altar to *Adonai*, who had appeared to him.

From there he moved to the mountain to the east of Beth-El and erected his tent (with Beth-El to the west and Ai to the east).

There he built an altar to *Adonai* and called on the Name of *Adonai*. So Abram kept on journeying southward.

Genesis 12:1-9

Now Lot, who was going with Abram, also had sheep and cattle and tents, so that the land could not support them living together, because their possessions were many, and they were not able to stay together.

Genesis 13:5-6

So Lot chose for himself the whole area surrounding the Jordan. Lot journeyed to the east, and they separated from each other. Abram dwelled in the land of Canaan, and Lot dwelled in the cities of the valley. And he moved his tent from place to place near Sodom.

Genesis 13:11-12

After these things the word of *Adonai* came to Abram in a vision saying, "Do not fear, Abram. I am your shield, your very great reward."

But Abram said, "My Lord *Adonai*, what will You give me, since I am living without children, and the heir of my household is Eliezer of Damascus?"

Then Abram said, "Look! You have given me no seed, so a house-born servant is my heir."

Then behold, the word of *Adonai* came to him saying, "This one will not be your heir, but in fact, one who will come from your own body will be your heir."

He took him outside and said, "Look up now, at the sky, and count the stars—if you are able to count them." Then He said to him, "So shall your seed be."

Then he believed in *Adonai* and He reckoned it to him as righteousness.

Then He said to him, "I am *Adonai* who brought you out from Ur of the Chaldeans, in order to give you this land to inherit it."

So he said, "My Lord *Adonai*, how will I know that I will inherit it?"

Then He said to him, "Bring Me a three year old young cow, a three year old she-goat, a three year old ram, a turtle-dove and a young bird."
So he brought all these to Him and cut them in half, and put each piece opposite the other; but he did not cut the birds. Then birds of prey came down upon the carcasses, but Abram drove them away.

Genesis 15:1-11

When the sun set and it became dark, behold, there was a smoking oven and a fiery torch that passed between these pieces.
On that day *Adonai* cut a covenant with Abram, saying, "I give this land to your seed, from the river of Egypt to the great river, the Euphrates River: the Kenite, the Kenizzites, the Kadmonites, the Hittites, the Perizzites, the Raphaites, the Amorites, the Canaanites, the Girgashites, and the Jebusites."

Genesis 15:17-21

When Abram was 99 years old, *Adonai* appeared to Abram, and He said to him, "I am *El Shaddai*. Continually walk before Me and you will be blameless. My heart's desire is to make My covenant between Me and you, and then I will multiply you exceedingly much."

Abram fell on his face, and God spoke with him, saying, "For My part, because My covenant is with you, you will be the father of a multitude of nations.

No longer will your name be Abram, but your name will be Abraham, because I make you the father of a multitude of nations. Yes, I will make you exceedingly fruitful, and I will make you into nations, and kings will come forth from you. Yes, I will establish My covenant between Me and you and your seed after you throughout their generations for an everlasting covenant, in order to be your God and your seed's God after you.

I will give to you and to your seed after you the land where you are an outsider —the whole land of Canaan—as an everlasting possession, and I will be their God."

Genesis 17:1-8

He took him outside and said, "Look up now, at the sky, and count the stars—if you are able to count them." Then He said to him, "So shall your seed be." Then he believed in ADONAI and He reckoned it to him as righteousness.
From Genesis 15:5-6 TLV ©2018, image #6/54

7. God Keeps His Promise

Then ADONAI visited Sarah just as He had said, and ADONAI did for Sarah just as He had spoken. So Sarah became pregnant and gave birth to a son for Abraham in his old age, at the appointed time that God had told him. Abraham named his son who was born to him—whom Sarah bore for him—Isaac.

Genesis 21:1-3

The child grew and was weaned—Abraham made a big feast on the day Isaac was weaned. But Sarah saw the son of Hagar the Egyptian whom she had born to Abraham—making fun.

So she said to Abraham, "Drive out this female slave and her son, for the son of this female slave will not be an heir with my son—with Isaac."

Now the matter was very displeasing in Abraham's eyes on account of his son. But God said to Abraham, "Do not be displeased about the boy and your slave woman. Whatever Sarah says to you, listen to her voice. For through Isaac shall your seed be called. "

Genesis 21:8-12

Now these are the genealogies of Isaac, Abraham's son. Abraham fathered Isaac. Isaac was 40 years old when he took for himself Rebekah, the daughter of Bethuel the Aramean from Paddan-aram, the sister of Laban the Aramean, to be his wife. Isaac prayed to ADONAI on behalf of his wife because she was barren. ADONAI answered his plea and his wife Rebekah became pregnant.

Genesis 25:19-21

When the boys grew up, Esau became a man knowledgeable in hunting, an outdoorsman, while Jacob was a mild man, remaining in tents.

Genesis 25:27

Now Jacob cooked a stew. When Esau came in from the field, he was exhausted, so Esau said to Jacob, "Please feed me some of this really red stuff, because I'm exhausted"—that is why he is called Edom.

So Jacob said, "Sell your birthright to me today."

Esau said, "Look, I'm about to die. Of whatever use is this to me—a birthright?"

Jacob said, "Make a pledge to me now."

So he made a pledge to him, and sold his birthright to Jacob. Then Jacob gave Esau bread and lentil stew, and he ate and drank, then got up and left. So Esau despised his birthright.

Genesis 25:29-34

Now there was a famine in the land—aside from the previous famine that happened in Abraham's days. So Isaac went to King Abimelech of the Philistines, to Gerar.

Then ADONAI appeared to him and said, "Do not go down to Egypt. Dwell in the land about which I tell you. Live as an outsider in this land and I will be with you and bless you—for to you and to your seed I give all these lands—and I will confirm my pledge that I swore to Abraham your father.

I will multiply your seed like the stars of the sky and I will give your seed all these lands. And in your seed all the nations of the earth will continually be blessed, because Abraham listened to My voice and kept My charge, My *mitzvot*, My decrees, and My instructions."
So Isaac stayed in Gerar.

Genesis 26:1-6

He went up from there to Beer-sheba. ADONAI appeared to him that night and said, "I am the God of your father Abraham. Do not be afraid, for I am with you, and I will bless you and multiply your seed for the sake of Abraham my servant."

So he built an altar there and called on the Name of ADONAI. He pitched his tent there and Isaac's servants hollowed out a well there.

Genesis 26:23-25

So Isaac called for Jacob, blessed him, commanded him and said to him, "Don't take a wife from the daughters of Canaan. Get up, go to Paddan-aram, to the house of Bethuel, your mother's father, and take for yourself a wife from there, from the daughters of Laban, your mother's brother.

Now may *El Shaddai* bless you and make you fruitful and multiply you so that you will become an assembly of peoples. And may he give you the blessing of Abraham, to you and to your seed with you that you may take possession of the land of your sojourn, which God gave to Abraham."

Genesis 28:1-4

Then Jacob left Beer-sheba and went toward Haran. He happened upon a certain place and spent the night there, for the sun had set.

So he took one of the stones from the place and put it by his head and lay down in that place. He dreamed: All of a sudden, there was a stairway set up on the earth and its top reaching to the heavens—and behold, angels of God going up and down on it!

Surprisingly, ADONAI was standing on top of it and He said, "I am ADONAI, the God of your father Abraham and the God of Isaac.

The land on which you lie, I will give it to you and to your seed. Your seed will be as the dust of the land, and you will burst forth to the west and to the east and to the north and to the south. And in you all the families of the earth will be blessed—and in your seed.

Behold, I am with you, and I will watch over you wherever you go, and I will bring you back to this land, for I will not forsake you until I have done what I promised you."

Jacob woke up from his sleep and said, "Undoubtedly, ADONAI is in this place—and I was unaware." So he was afraid and said, "How fearsome this place is! This is none other than the House of God—this must be the gate of heaven!"

Early in the morning Jacob got up and took the stone, which he had placed by his head, and set it up as a memorial stone and poured oil on top of it. He called the name of that place Beth-El (though originally the city's name was Luz).

Then Jacob made a vow saying, "If God will be with me and watch over me on this way that I am going, and provide me food to eat and clothes to wear, and I return in *shalom* to my father's house, then ADONAI will be my God. So this stone which I set up as a memorial stone will become God's House, and of everything You provide me I will definitely give a tenth of it to You."

Genesis 28:10-22

He dreamed: All of a sudden, there was a stairway set up on the earth and its top reaching to the heavens
—and behold, angels of God going up and down on it!

From Genesis 28:12 TLV ©2018, image #7/54

31

8. God Reunites Brothers

God appeared to Jacob again, after he returned from Paddan-aram, and He blessed him. God said to him: "Your name was Jacob. No longer will your name be Jacob, for your name will be Israel." So He named him Israel.

God also said to him: "I am *El Shaddai*. Be fruitful and multiply. A nation and an assembly of nations will come from you. From your loins will come forth kings. The land that I gave to Abraham and to Isaac - I give it to you, and to your seed after you I will give the land."

Genesis 35:9-12

...Now Jacob had twelve sons.

Genesis 35:22b

Now Israel loved Joseph more than all his other sons because he was the son of his old age. So he had made him a long-sleeved tunic. When his brothers saw that their father loved him more than all his brothers, they hated him and could not speak to him in *shalom*. Then Joseph dreamed a dream and told his brothers—and they hated him even more.

He said to them, "Please listen to this dream I dreamed. There we were binding sheaves in the middle of the field. All of a sudden, my sheaf arose and stood upright. And behold, your sheaves gathered around and bowed down to my sheaf."

"Will you truly be a king over us?" his brothers said to him. "Will you really rule over us?" So they hated him even more because of his dreams and because of his words.

Genesis 37:3-8

Then his brothers went to graze their father's flocks at Shechem. Israel said to Joseph, "Aren't your brothers grazing the flocks in Shechem? Come, let me send you to them."

"Here I am," he said to him. Then he said to him, "Go now, and check on the welfare of your brothers and the welfare of the flocks and bring word back to me."

Genesis 37:12-14

Now they saw him from a distance. Before he was close to them they plotted together against him in order to kill him.

They said to one another, "Here comes the master of dreams! Come on now! Let's kill him and throw him into one of those pits, so we can say that an evil animal devoured him. Then let's see what becomes of his dreams."

Genesis 37:18-20

Then Judah said to his brothers, "What profit is there if we kill our brother and cover up his blood? Come on! Let's sell him to the Ishmaelites. Let's not lay our hand on him - since he's our brother, our own flesh." His brothers listened to him.

When some men, Midianite merchants, passed by, they dragged Joseph up and out of the pit and they sold Joseph to the Ishmaelites for 20 pieces of silver, and they brought Joseph to Egypt.

Genesis 37:26-28

But ADONAI was with Joseph. So he became a successful man in the house of his master, the Egyptian. His master saw that ADONAI was with him and that ADONAI made everything he set his hand to successful.

Genesis 39:2-3

Then Joseph's master took him and put him in prison, the place where the king's prisoners were confined. So there he was, in the prison. But ADONAI was with Joseph and extended kindness to him and gave him favor in the eyes of the commander of the prison.

Genesis 39:20-21

Then Joseph said to Pharaoh, … "It is the word that I have already said to Pharaoh: what God is about to do, he has shown to Pharaoh. Seven years of abundance are about to come in the whole land of Egypt. Then seven years of famine will come up after them and all the abundance in the land of Egypt will be forgotten and the famine will consume the land.

Genesis 41:28-30

Then Pharaoh said to Joseph, "Since God has made all this known to you, there is no one as discerning and wise as you. You! You will be over my house, and all my people will pay homage to you. Only in relation to the throne will I be greater than you."

Genesis 41:39-40

The famine was over all the entire land, so Joseph opened up all that was among them and sold grain to Egypt. Then the famine became severe in the land of Egypt. Yet the whole world came to Egypt to buy grain—to Joseph—because the famine was severe in the whole world.

Genesis 41:56-57

The sons of Israel went to buy grain among the others who were coming, because the famine was in the land of Canaan. Now Joseph was the ruler over the land. He was the provider of grain for all the people of the earth. Then Joseph's brothers came and bowed down to him with faces to the ground. When Joseph saw his brothers, he recognized them, but he made himself unrecognizable to them. …

Genesis 42:5-7b

Now Joseph could no longer restrain himself in front of all those who were standing by him, so he cried out, "Get everyone away from me!" So no one stood with him when Joseph made himself known to his brothers. But he gave his voice to weeping so that the Egyptians heard, and Pharaoh's household heard.

Joseph said to his brothers, "I am Joseph! Is my father still alive?" And his brothers were unable to answer him because they were terrified at his presence.

Then Joseph said to his brothers, "Please come near me." So they came near. "I'm Joseph, your brother—the one you sold to Egypt," he said. "So now, don't be grieved and don't be angry in your own eyes that you sold me here—since it was for preserving life that God sent me here before you. For there has been two years of famine in the land, and there will be five more years yet with no plowing or harvesting. But God sent me ahead of you to ensure a remnant in the land and to keep you alive for a great escape. So now, it wasn't you, you didn't send me here, but God! And He made me as a father to Pharaoh, lord over his whole house and ruler over the entire land of Egypt.

Genesis 45:1-8

Then he fell upon his brother Benjamin's neck and wept while Benjamin wept upon his neck, and he kissed all his brothers and wept upon them. Finally after this, his brothers talked with him.

Genesis 45:14-15

"Thus you must say to Joseph: 'Please forgive, I beg you, the transgression of your brothers and their sin because they treated you wrongly.' Therefore, please forgive the transgression of the servants of the God of your father."

Then Joseph wept when they spoke to him, and his brothers also came and fell down before him and said, "Behold, we are your slaves!"

But Joseph said to them, "Don't be afraid. For am I in the place of God? Yes, you yourselves planned evil against me. God planned it for good, in order to bring about what it is this day—to preserve the lives of many people."

Genesis 50:17-20

"I'm Joseph, your brother—the one you sold to Egypt," he said. "So now, don't be grieved and don't be angry in your own eyes that you sold me here—since it was for preserving life that God sent me here before you.

From Genesis 45:4-5 TLV ©2018, image #8/54

9. God Rescues a Baby

Now these are the names of *Bnei-Yisrael* who came into Egypt with Jacob, each man with his family: Reuben, Simeon, Levi and Judah; Issachar, Zebulun and Benjamin; Dan, Naphtali, Gad and Asher.

The souls that came out of the line of Jacob numbered 70 in all, while Joseph was already in Egypt.

Then Joseph died, as did all his brothers and all that generation. Yet *Bnei-Yisrael* were fruitful, increased abundantly, multiplied and grew extremely numerous—so the land was filled with them.

Now there arose a new king over Egypt, who did not know Joseph.

He said to his people, "Look, the people of *Bnei-Yisrael* are too numerous and too powerful for us. Come, we must deal shrewdly with them, or else they will grow even more numerous, so that if war breaks out, they may join our enemies, fight against us, and then escape from the land."

So they set slave masters over them to afflict them with forced labor, and they built Pithom and Raamses as storage cities for Pharaoh. But the more they afflicted them, the more they multiplied and the more they spread. So the Egyptians dreaded the presence of *Bnei-Yisrael*.

They worked them harshly, and made their lives bitter with hard labor with mortar and brick, doing all sorts of work in the fields. In all their labors they worked them with cruelty.

Moreover the king of Egypt spoke to the Hebrew midwives, one of whom was named Shiphrah and the other Puah, and said, "When you help the Hebrew women during childbirth, look at the sex. If it's a son, then kill him, but if it's a daughter, she may live."

Yet the midwives feared God, so they did not do as the king of Egypt commanded them, but let the boys live.

So the king of Egypt summoned the midwives and said to them, "Why have you done this—let the boys live?"

The midwives told Pharaoh, "Because the Hebrew women are not like Egyptian women. They are like animals, and give birth before the midwife comes to them."

So God was good to the midwives, and the people multiplied, growing very numerous. Because the midwives feared God, He gave them families of their own.

But Pharaoh charged all his people saying, "You are to cast every son that is born into the river, but let every daughter live."

Exodus 1:1-22

Now a man from the house of Levi took as his wife a daughter of Levi. The woman conceived and gave birth to a son.

Now when she saw that he was delightful, she hid him for three months. But when she could no longer hide him, she took a basket of papyrus reeds, coated it with tar and pitch, put the child inside, and laid it in the reeds by the bank of the Nile.

His sister stood off at a distance to see what would happen to him.

Then the daughter of Pharaoh came down to bathe, while her maidens walked along by the riverside. When she saw the basket among the reeds, she sent her handmaiden to fetch it. When she opened it, she saw the child—a baby boy crying!

She had compassion on him and said, "This is one of the Hebrew children."

Then his sister said to Pharaoh's daughter, "Should I go and call a nurse from the Hebrews to nurse the child for you?"

Pharaoh's daughter told her, "Go!"

So the girl went and called the child's mother. Then Pharaoh's daughter said to her, "Take this child and nurse him for me, and I will pay you your wages."

So the woman took the child and nursed him. After the boy grew older she brought him to Pharaoh's daughter and he became her son.

So she named him Moses saying, "Because I drew him out of the water."

Now it happened in those days, after Moses had grown up, that he went out to his brothers and saw their burdens. He noticed an Egyptian beating a Hebrew, one of his own people. So he looked around and when he saw that there was nobody, he killed the Egyptian and hid him in the sand. Then he went out the following day, and saw two Hebrew men fighting.
So he said to the guilty one, "Why are you beating your companion?"

But the man answered, "Who made you a ruler and a judge over us? Are you saying you're going to kill me—just as you killed the Egyptian?"

Then Moses was afraid, and thought, "For sure the deed had become known."

When Pharaoh heard about this, he tried to kill Moses. But Moses fled from Pharaoh and settled in the land of Midian, where he sat down by a well.

Now the priest of Midian had seven daughters who came and drew water. They filled the troughs to water their father's flock. But shepherds came and drove them away, so Moses stood up, helped them and watered their flock.

When they came to Reuel their father, he said, "How come you've returned so soon today?"
So they told him, "An Egyptian delivered us out of the hand of the shepherds. He also drew water for us and watered the flock."

"Where is he then?" he said to his daughters. "Why did you leave the man behind? Invite him to have some food to eat!"

Moses was content to stay on with the man. Later he gave Moses his daughter Zipporah. She gave birth to a son and he named him Gershom, saying, "I have been an outsider in a foreign land."

Exodus 2:1-22

Then the daughter of Pharaoh came down to bathe, while her maidens walked along by the riverside. When she saw the basket among the reeds, she sent her handmaiden to fetch it. When she opened it, she saw the child—a baby boy crying!
From Exodus 2:6 TLV ©2018, image #9/54

10. God Calls to Moses

Now it came about over the course of those many days that the king of Egypt died. *Bnei-Yisrael* groaned because of their slavery. They cried out and their cry from slavery went up to God. God heard their sobbing and remembered His covenant with Abraham, Isaac, and Jacob. God saw *Bnei-Yisrael*, and He was concerned about them.

Genesis 2:23-25

Now Moses was tending the flock of his father-in-law Jethro, the priest of Midian. So he led the flock to the farthest end of the wilderness, coming to the mountain of God, Horeb. Then the angel of ADONAI appeared to him in a flame of fire from within a bush. So he looked and saw the bush burning with fire, yet it was not consumed.

Moses thought, "I will go now, and see this great sight. Why is the bush not burnt?"

When ADONAI saw that he turned to look, He called to him out of the midst of the bush and said, "Moses, Moses!"

So he answered, "*Hineni.*"

Then He said, "Come no closer. Take your sandals off your feet, for the place where you are standing is holy ground." Moreover He said, "I am the God of your father, the God of Abraham, Isaac and Jacob."

So Moses hid his face, because he was afraid to look at God.

Then ADONAI said, "I have surely seen the affliction of My people who are in Egypt, and have heard their cry because of their slave masters, for I know their pains.

So I have come down to deliver them out of the hand of the Egyptians, to bring them up out of that land into a good and large land, a land flowing with milk and honey, into the place of the Canaanites, Hittites, Amorites, Perizzites, Hivites and Jebusites.

Now behold, the cry of *Bnei-Yisrael* has come to Me. Moreover I have seen the oppression that the Egyptians have inflicted on them. Come now, I will send you to Pharaoh, so that you may bring My people *Bnei-Yisrael* out from Egypt."

But Moses said to God, "Who am I, that I should go to Pharaoh, and bring *Bnei-Yisrael* out of Egypt?"

So He said, "I will surely be with you. So that will be the sign to you that it is I who have sent you. When you have brought the people out of Egypt: you will worship God on this mountain."

But Moses said to God, "Suppose I go to *Bnei-Yisrael* and say to them, 'The God of your fathers has sent me to you,' and they ask me, 'What is His Name?' What should I say to them?"

God answered Moses, "I AM WHO I AM."

Then He said, "You are to say to *Bnei-Yisrael*, 'I AM' has sent me to you."

God also said to Moses: "You are to say to *Bnei-Yisrael*, ADONAI, the God of your fathers, the God of Abraham, Isaac and Jacob, has sent me to you. This is My Name forever, and the Name by which I should be remembered from generation to generation.

"Go now, gather the elders of Israel together, and say to them:

'ADONAI, the God of your fathers—the God of Abraham, Isaac and Jacob—has appeared to me, saying, I have been paying close attention to you and have seen what is done to you in Egypt.

So I promise I will bring you up out of the affliction of Egypt, into the land of the Canaanites, Hittites, Amorites, Perizzites, Hivites and Jebusites, to a land flowing with milk and honey.'

"They will listen to your voice. So you will go, you along with the elders of Israel, to the king of Egypt, and say to him:

'ADONAI, the God of the Hebrews, has met with us. Now please let us take a three-day journey into the wilderness, so that we may sacrifice to ADONAI our God.'

Nevertheless, I know that the king of Egypt will not let you go, except by a mighty hand. So I will stretch out My hand and strike Egypt with all My wonders that I will do in the midst of it. After that, he will let you go. Then I shall grant these people favor in the eyes of the Egyptians. So it will happen that when you go, you will not leave empty-handed.

Every woman is to ask her neighbor and the woman who lives in her house for silver and gold jewelry and clothing. You will put them on your sons and your daughters. So you will plunder the Egyptians."

Exodus 3:1-22

Then Moses said, "But look, they will not believe me or listen to my voice. They will say, 'ADONAI has not appeared to you.'"

So ADONAI said to him, "What is that in your hand?"

"A staff," he said. Then He said, "Cast it on the ground." When he cast it to the ground, it became a serpent, so Moses fled from before it.

Then ADONAI said to Moses, "Stretch out your hand, and take it by the tail." So he put out his hand, laid hold of it, and it became a staff in his hand.

"This is so that they may believe ADONAI, the God of their fathers—the God of Abraham, Isaac and Jacob—has appeared to you."

ADONAI also said to him, "Now put your hand within your cloak." So he put his hand inside, and when he took it out, his hand had *tza-ra'at*—white as snow.

Then He said, "Put your hand back into your cloak."

So he put his hand back in, and when he took it out it was restored again as the rest of his skin.

Then He said, "If they do not believe you, or listen to the voice of the first sign, they will believe the message of the latter sign. But if they do not believe even these two signs nor listen to your voice, you are to take the water of the river and pour it on the dry land. The water which you take out of the river will become blood on the ground."

Exodus 4:1-9

Then He said, "Come no closer. Take your sandals off your feet, for the place where you are standing is holy ground."
Moreover He said, "I am the God of your father, the God of Abraham, Isaac and Jacob."
From Exodus 3:5-6 TLV ©2018, image #10/54

11. God Challenges Pharaoh

Now ADONAI said to Aaron, "Go into the wilderness to meet Moses."

So he went and met him at the mountain of God, and kissed him. Then Moses told Aaron all the words of ADONAI with which He had been sent, along with all the signs that He had commanded him to do.

Then Moses and Aaron went and assembled all the elders of Bnei-Yisrael. Aaron spoke all the words that ADONAI had spoken to Moses and did the signs in the sight of the people.

So the people believed. When they heard that ADONAI had remembered Bnei-Yisrael and had seen their affliction, they bowed their heads and worshipped.

Exodus 4:27-31

Afterward, Moses and Aaron went and said to Pharaoh, "This is what ADONAI, God of Israel, says: Let My people go, so that they may hold a feast for Me in the wilderness."

But Pharaoh said, "Who is ADONAI, that I should listen to His voice and let Israel go? I do not know ADONAI, and besides, I will not let Israel go."

Exodus 5:1-2

Therefore say to Bnei-Yisrael: I am ADONAI, and I will bring you out from under the burdens of the Egyptians. I will deliver you from their bondage, and I will redeem you with an outstretched arm and with great judgments.

Exodus 6:6

ADONAI said to Moses, "Say to Aaron: Take your staff and stretch out your hand over the waters of Egypt, over their rivers, over their streams, over their pools and over all their ponds, so that they become blood. There will be blood throughout all the land of Egypt, even in wooden and stone containers."

So Moses and Aaron did as ADONAI commanded. He lifted up the staff and struck the waters that were in the river in the sight of Pharaoh and his servants, and all the waters of the Nile turned to blood.

Exodus 7:19-20

But the magicians of Egypt did the same with their secret arts. So Pharaoh's heart was hardened, and he did not listen to them—just as ADONAI had said.

Exodus 7:22

Then ADONAI told Moses, "Say to Aaron: Stretch out your hand with your staff over the rivers, canals and pools, and cause frogs to come up over the land of Egypt."

Exodus 8:1

Then Pharaoh called for Moses and Aaron and said, "Pray to ADONAI, that He would take the frogs away from me and from my people. Then I will let the people go so they may sacrifice to ADONAI." …

Exodus 8:4

But when Pharaoh saw that there was relief, he hardened his heart and did not listen to them - just as ADONAI had said.

So ADONAI said to Moses, "Tell Aaron, 'Stretch out your staff and strike the dust of the earth, and it will become gnats throughout all the land of Egypt.'"

Exodus 8:11-12

So the magicians said to Pharaoh, "This is the finger of God."

But Pharaoh's heart was hardened, and he did not listen to them - just as ADONAI had said.

Then ADONAI said to Moses, "Rise up early in the morning and stand before Pharaoh. As he comes to the water say to him, This is what ADONAI says:

Let My people go, that they may serve Me. Or else, if you do not let My people go, I will send the swarm of flies on you and on your servants, on your people and into your houses. The houses of the Egyptians will be full of the swarm of flies including the ground that they stand on.

"But on that day I will set apart the land of Goshen, where My people are dwelling—except no swarm of flies will be there—so that you may know that I, ADONAI, am in the midst of the earth. I will make a distinction between My people and your people. By tomorrow this sign will happen."

Exodus 8:14-19

... All the cattle of Egypt died, yet of the cattle of *Bnei-Yisrael*, not one died.

Exodus 9:6b

Then ADONAI said to Moses and Aaron, "Take handfuls of soot from the furnace, and have Moses throw it heavenward in the sight of Pharaoh. It will become fine dust over all the land of Egypt, and will become boils erupting with sores on both men and animals throughout all the land."

Exodus 9:8-9

Then ADONAI said to Moses, "Stretch out your hand toward heaven and let there be hail in all the land of Egypt, on people, animals and every plant of the field, throughout all the land."

Exodus 9:22

Only in the land of Goshen, where *Bnei-Yisrael* were, was there no hail.

Exodus 9:26

So Pharaoh's heart was hardened and he did not let *Bnei-Yisrael* go—just as ADONAI had said by Moses' hand.

Exodus 9:35

Then ADONAI said to Moses, "Stretch out your hand over the land of Egypt for the locusts, so they may come up onto Egypt and eat every plant in the land—everything the hail has left."

Exodus 10:12

Then ADONAI said to Moses, "Stretch out your hand toward heaven, and there will be darkness over the land of Egypt—a darkness that may be felt." So Moses stretched out his hand toward heaven, and there was a thick darkness in all the land of Egypt for three days. They could not see one another, nor could anyone rise from his place for three days. Yet all *Bnei-Yisrael* had light within their dwellings.

Exodus 10:21-23

So Moses and Aaron did all these wonders before Pharaoh, yet ADONAI hardened Pharaoh's heart, so he did not let *Bnei-Yisrael* go out of his land.

Exodus 11:10

Then Moses called for all the elders of Israel and said to them, "Go, select lambs for your families and slaughter the Passover lamb. You are to take a bundle of hyssop, dip it in the blood that is in the basin, and apply it to the crossbeam and two doorposts with the blood from the basin. None of you may go out the door of his house until morning. ADONAI will pass through to strike down the Egyptians, but when He sees the blood on the crossbeam and the two doorposts, ADONAI will pass over that door, and will not allow the destroyer to come into your houses to strike you down. Also you are to observe this event as an eternal ordinance, for you and your children.

Exodus 12:21-24

But ADONAI hardened Pharaoh's heart, and he was unwilling to let them go. So Pharaoh said to him, "Go away from me! Take heed never to see my face again, because on the day you do, you will die!"
"Right!" Moses said. "You said it! May I never see your face again!"
From Exodus 10:27-29 TLV ©2018, image #11/54

12. God Births a Nation

After Pharaoh had let the people go, God did not lead them along the road to the land of the Philistines, although that was nearby, for God said, "The people might change their minds if they see war and return to Egypt."

So God led the people around by the way of the wilderness to the Sea of Reeds, and *Bnei-Yisrael* went up out of the land of Egypt armed. Moses also took the bones of Joseph with him, for he had made *Bnei-Yisrael* swear an oath saying, "God will surely remember you, and then you are to carry my bones away with you."

So they journeyed from Succoth and encamped in Etham, on the edge of the wilderness. ADONAI went before them in a pillar of cloud by day to lead the way and in a pillar of fire by night to give them light.

So they could travel both day and night. The pillar of cloud by day and the pillar of fire by night never departed from the people.

Exodus 13:17-22

ADONAI spoke to Moses saying, "Speak to *Bnei-Yisrael*, so that they turn back and encamp before Pi-hahiroth, between Migdol and the sea. You are to camp by the sea, opposite Baal-zephon. Pharaoh will say concerning *Bnei-Yisrael*, 'They are wandering aimlessly in the land—the wilderness has shut them in!' I will harden Pharaoh's heart, so he will follow after them. Then I will be glorified over Pharaoh along with all his army, and the Egyptians will know that I am ADONAI."

So they did so.

When the king of Egypt was told that the people had fled, Pharaoh and his servants had a change of heart toward the people, and they said, "What is this we have done, that we let Israel go from serving us?"

So he prepared his chariots and took his people with him. He took 600 of the finest chariots, along with all other chariots of Egypt, and captains over them.

ADONAI hardened the heart of Pharaoh king of Egypt, so he pursued *Bnei-Yisrael*, for *Bnei-Yisrael* went out with a high hand.

Exodus 14:1-8

When Pharaoh drew near, *Bnei-Yisrael* lifted up their eyes, and behold, the Egyptians were marching after them! So they were terrified, and *Bnei-Yisrael* cried out to ADONAI.

Exodus 14:10

But Moses said to the people, "Don't be afraid! Stand still, and see the salvation of ADONAI, which He will perform for you today.

You have seen the Egyptians today, but you will never see them again, ever! ADONAI will fight for you, while you hold your peace."

Then ADONAI said to Moses, "Why are you crying to Me? Tell *Bnei-Yisrael* to go forward. Lift up your staff, stretch out your hand over the sea, and divide it. Then *Bnei-Yisrael* will go into the midst of the sea on dry ground.

Then I, behold, I will harden the hearts of the Egyptians, and they will go in after them, so that I will be glorified over Pharaoh and all his army, his chariots and his horsemen.

Then the Egyptians will know that I am ADONAI, when I have been glorified over Pharaoh, his chariots and his horsemen."

Then the angel of God, who went before the camp of Israel, moved and went behind them. Also the pillar of cloud moved from in front and stood behind them, and so came between the camp of Egypt and the camp of Israel—there was the cloud and the darkness over here, yet it gave light by night over there—neither one came near the other all night long.

Then Moses stretched out his hand over the sea. *ADONAI* drove the sea back with a strong east wind throughout the night and turned the sea into dry land. So the waters were divided.

Then *Bnei-Yisrael* went into the midst of the sea on the dry ground, while the waters were like walls to them on their right and on their left. But the Egyptians pursued and went in after them into the midst of the sea, all Pharaoh's horses, his chariots and his horsemen.

Now it came about during the morning watch that *ADONAI* looked at the army of the Egyptians through the pillar of fire and cloud and caused the army of the Egyptians to panic.

He took off their chariot wheels and caused them to drive heavily, so that the Egyptians said, "Get away from the presence of Israel! For *ADONAI* fights for them against the Egyptians!"

Then *ADONAI* said to Moses, "Stretch out your hand over the sea, so that the waters come back upon the Egyptians, over their chariots and their horsemen."

So Moses stretched his hand out over the waters, and the sea returned to its strength at the break of dawn. The Egyptians were fleeing from it, but *ADONAI* overthrew them in the midst of the sea.

The waters returned and covered the chariots, the horsemen and the entire army of Pharaoh that went after them into the sea. Not one of them remained.

But *Bnei-Yisrael* had walked on dry land in the midst of the sea, and the waters were like walls to them on their right hand and on their left.

So *ADONAI* saved Israel that day out of the hand of the Egyptians, and Israel saw the Egyptians dead on the seashore. When Israel saw the great work that *ADONAI* did over the Egyptians, the people feared *ADONAI*, and they believed in *ADONAI* and in His servant Moses.

Exodus 14:13-31

Then Moses and *Bnei-Yisrael* sang this song to *ADONAI* :

I will sing to *ADONAI*,

for He is highly exalted!

The horse and its rider

He has thrown into the sea.

ADONAI is my strength and song,

and He has become my salvation.

This is my God, and I will glorify Him,

my father's God, and I will exalt Him.

ADONAI is a warrior—*ADONAI* is His Name!

Pharaoh's chariots and his army

He has hurled into the sea,

and his chosen captains have sunk

into the Sea of Reeds.

The deeps cover them.

They sank to the depths like a stone.

Your right hand, *ADONAI* ,

is glorious in power.

Your right hand, *ADONAI*,

dashes the enemy to pieces.

Exodus 15:1-6

Who is like You, *ADONAI*, among the gods?

Who is like You, glorious in holiness,

awesome in praises, doing wonders?

Exodus 15:11

But *Bnei-Yisrael* had walked on dry land in the midst of the sea, and the waters were like walls to them on their right hand and on their left.
From Exodus 14:29 TLV ©2018, image #12/54

51

13. God Covenants with *Bnei-Yisrael*

Then Moses led Israel onward from the Sea of Reeds. They went out into the wilderness of Shur. But they travelled three days in the wilderness and found no water.

Exodus 15:22

Then they came to Elim, where there were twelve springs of water and seventy palm trees. So they camped there by the waters.

Exodus 15:27

They journeyed on from Elim, and the entire community of *Bnei-Yisrael* came to the wilderness of Sin, which is between Elim and Sinai, on the fifteenth day of the second month after leaving the land of Egypt.

Exodus 16:1

Then ADONAI said to Moses, "Behold, I will rain bread from heaven for you. The people will go out and gather a day's portion every day, so that I can test them to find out whether they will walk according to My *Torah* or not.

So on the sixth day, when they prepare what they bring in, it will be twice as much as they gather day by day."

Exodus 16:4-5

Then Moses said, "Eat that today, because today is a *Shabbat* to ADONAI. Today you will not find it in the field. You are to gather it for six days, but the seventh day is the *Shabbat*, and there will be none."

Exodus 16:25-26

The house of Israel named it *manna*. It was white like coriander seed and tasted like wafers made with honey.

Then Moses said, "This is what ADONAI has commanded. Let a full omer of it be kept throughout your generations, so that they may see the bread with which I fed you in the wilderness, when I brought you out from the land of Egypt."

Exodus 16:31-32

In the third month after *Bnei-Yisrael* had gone out of the land of Egypt, that same day they arrived at the wilderness of Sinai. They travelled from Rephidim, came into to the wilderness of Sinai, and set up camp in the wilderness. Israel camped there, right in front of the mountain.

Moses went up to God, and ADONAI called to him from the mountain saying, "Say this to the house of Jacob, and tell *Bnei-Yisrael*,

'You have seen what I did to the Egyptians, and how I carried you on eagle's wings and brought you to Myself. Now then, if you listen closely to My voice, and keep My covenant, then you will be My own treasure from among all people, for all the earth is Mine. So as for you, you will be to Me a kingdom of *kohanim* and a holy nation.'

These are the words which you are to speak to *Bnei-Yisrael*."

So Moses went, called for the elders of the people, and put before them all these words that ADONAI had commanded him.

All the people answered together and said, "Everything that ADONAI has spoken, we will do."

Then Moses reported the words of the people to ADONAI.

ADONAI said to Moses, "I am about to come to you in a thick cloud, so that the people will hear when I speak with you and believe you forever." Then Moses told the words of the people to ADONAI.

ADONAI said to Moses, "Go to the people, and sanctify them today and tomorrow. Let them wash their clothing. Be ready for the third day. For on the third day ADONAI will come down upon Mount Sinai in the sight of all the people.

Exodus 19:1-11

In the morning of the third day, there was thundering and lightning, a thick cloud on the mountain, and the blast of an exceedingly loud *shofar*. All the people in the camp trembled.

Then Moses brought the people out of the camp to meet God, and they stood at the lowest part of the mountain.

Now the entire Mount Sinai was in smoke, because ADONAI had descended upon it in fire. The smoke ascended like the smoke of a furnace. The whole mountain quaked greatly.

When the sound of the *shofar* grew louder and louder, Moses spoke, and God answered him with a thunderous sound. Then ADONAI came down onto Mount Sinai, to the top of the mountain. ADONAI called Moses to the top of the mountain, so Moses went up.

Exodus 19:16-20

All the people witnessed the thundering and the lightning, and the sound of the *shofar*, and the mountain smoking.

When the people saw it, they trembled and stood far off. So they said to Moses, "You, speak to us, and we will listen, but do not let God speak to us, or we will die."

So Moses said to the people, "Do not be afraid, for God has come to test you, so that His fear may be in you, so that you do not sin." The people stood far off, while Moses drew near to the thick darkness where God was.

Exodus 20:18-21

So Moses came and told the people all the words of ADONAI as well as all the ordinances. All the people answered with one voice and said, "All the words which ADONAI has spoken, we will do."

So Moses wrote down all the words of ADONAI, then rose up early in the morning, and built an altar below the mountain, along with twelve pillars for the twelve tribes of Israel.

Exodus 24:3-4

He took the Scroll of the Covenant and read it in the hearing of the people.

Again they said, "All that ADONAI has spoken, we will do and obey."

Then Moses took the blood, sprinkled it on the people, and said, "Behold the blood of the covenant, which ADONAI has cut with you, in agreement with all these words."

Exodus 24:7-8

Then ADONAI said to Moses, "Come up to Me on the mountain and stay there, and I will give you the tablets of stone with the *Torah* and the *mitzvot*, which I have written so that you may instruct them."

Exodus 24:12

When Moses went up on the mountain, the cloud covered it. The glory of ADONAI settled upon Mount Sinai, and the cloud covered it for six days. Then on the seventh day He called to Moses out of the midst of the cloud.

The appearance of the glory of ADONAI was like a consuming fire on the top of the mountain in the sight of *Bnei-Yisrael*. So Moses entered into the midst of the cloud and went up onto the mountain. Moses was on the mountain 40 days and 40 nights.

Exodus 24:15-18

He took the Scroll of the Covenant and read it in the hearing of the people. Again they said, "All that ADONAI has spoken, we will do and obey." Then Moses took the blood, sprinkled it on the people, and said, "Behold the blood of the covenant, which ADONAI has cut with you, in agreement with all these words."

From Exodus 24:7-8 TLV ©2018, image #13/54

14. God Teaches His People

Then God spoke all these words saying,

א "I am ADONAI your God, who brought you out of the land of Egypt, out of the house of bondage.

ב You shall have no other gods before Me.

ג Do not make for yourself a graven image, or any likeness of anything that is in heaven above or on the earth below or in the water under the earth. Do not bow down to them, do not let anyone make you serve them. For I, ADONAI your God, am a jealous God, bringing the iniquity of the fathers upon the children to the third and fourth generations of those who hate Me, but showing lovingkindness to the thousands of generations of those who love Me and keep My *mitzvot*.

ד You must not take the Name of ADONAI your God in vain, for ADONAI will not hold him guiltless that takes His Name in vain.

ה Remember *Yom Shabbat*, to keep it holy. You are to work six days, and do all your work, but the seventh day is a *Shabbat* to ADONAI your God. In it you shall not do any work—

not you, nor your son, your daughter, your male servant, your female servant, your cattle, nor the outsider that is within your gates. For in six days ADONAI made heaven and earth, the sea, and all that is in them, and rested on the seventh day. Thus ADONAI blessed *Yom Shabbat*, and made it holy.

ו Honor your father and your mother, so that your days may be long upon the land which ADONAI your God is giving you.

ז Do not murder.

ח Do not commit adultery.

ט Do not steal.

י Do not bear false witness against your neighbor.

כ Do not covet your neighbor's house, your neighbor's wife, his manservant, his maidservant, his ox, his donkey, or anything that is your neighbor's."

Exodus 20:1-17

"Three times in the year you are to celebrate a festival for Me. You are to observe the Feast of *Matzot*. For seven days you will eat *matzot* as I commanded you, at the time appointed in the month Aviv, for that is when you came out from Egypt.

No one is to appear before Me empty-handed.

"Also you are to observe the Feast of Harvest, the firstfruits of your labors that you sow in the field, as well as the Feast of the Ingathering at the end of the year, when you gather your crops from the field. Three times in the year all your men are to appear before *ADONAI Elohim*."

Exodus 23:14-17

"Behold, I am sending an angel before you, to guard you on the way and to bring you into the place that I have prepared. Watch for Him and listen to His voice.

Do not rebel against Him because He will not pardon your transgression, for My Name is in Him. But if you listen closely to His voice, and do everything I say, I will be an enemy to your enemies and an adversary to your adversaries."

Exodus 23:20-22

"You are to serve *ADONAI* your God, and He will bless your food and your water. Moreover I will take sickness away from your midst. None will miscarry nor be barren in your land, and I will fill up the number of your days."

Exodus 23:25-26

"I will set your border from the Sea of Reeds to the sea of the Philistines, and from the wilderness to the Euphrates River. For I will deliver the inhabitants of the land into your hand, and you are to drive them out before you. Make no covenant with them or with their gods. They must not dwell in your land and cause you to sin against Me, for if you worship their gods, they will be a snare to you."

Exodus 23:31-33

ADONAI spoke to Moses saying, "Tell *Bnei-Yisrael* to take up an offering for Me. From anyone whose heart compels him you are to take My offering."

Exodus 25:1-2

"Have them make a Sanctuary for Me, so that I may dwell among them. You are to make it all precisely according to everything that I show you—the pattern of the Tabernacle and the pattern of all the furnishings within—just so you must make it."

Exodus 25:8-9

Then *ADONAI* spoke to Moses saying, "See, I have called by name Bezalel son of Uri son of Hur, of the tribe of Judah, and I have filled him with the Spirit of God, with wisdom, understanding and knowledge in all kinds of craftsmanship, to make ingenious designs, to forge with gold, silver and bronze, as well as cutting stones for setting and carving wood, to work in all manner of craftsmanship. Also look, I Myself have appointed with him Oholiab son of Ahisamach, of the tribe of Dan. Within the hearts of all who are wise-hearted I have placed skill, so that they may make everything that I have commanded you: ... "

Exodus 31:1-6

So *Bnei-Yisrael* is to keep the *Shabbat*, to observe the *Shabbat* throughout their generations as a perpetual covenant. It is a sign between Me and *Bnei-Yisrael* forever, for in six days *ADONAI* made heaven and earth, and on the seventh day He ceased from work and rested.'"

When He had finished speaking with him on Mount Sinai, He gave the two tablets of the Testimony to Moses—tablets of stone, written by the finger of God.

Exodus 31:16-18

Now when the people saw that Moses delayed coming down from the mountain, they gathered around Aaron and said to him, "Get up, make us gods who will go before us. As for this Moses, the man that brought us up out of the land of Egypt, we do not know what's become of him!"

Exodus 32:1

Then *ADONAI* said to Moses, "Go down! For your people, whom you brought up out of the land of Egypt, have become debased."

Exodus 32:7

Then Moses turned and went down from the mountain, with the two tablets of the Testimony in his hand, tablets that were written on both sides, on one and on the other. The tablets were the work of God, and the writing was the writing of God, engraved on the tablets.

Exodus 32:15-16

Then Moses turned and went down from the mountain, with the two tablets of the Testimony in his hand, tablets that were written on both sides, on one and on the other. The tablets were the work of God, and the writing was the writing of God, engraved on the tablets.

From Exodus 32:15-16 TLV ©2018, image #14/54

15. God Visits His Tent

Then ADONAI spoke to Moses saying, "Speak now to Bnei-Yisrael saying, 'Surely you must keep My Shabbatot, for it is a sign between Me and you throughout your generations, so you may know that I am ADONAI who sanctifies you. Therefore you are to keep the Shabbat, because it is holy for you.

Exodus 31:12-14a

It is a sign between Me and Bnei-Yisrael forever, for in six days ADONAI made heaven and earth, and on the seventh day He ceased from work and rested.'" When He had finished speaking with him on Mount Sinai, He gave the two tablets of the Testimony to Moses—tablets of stone, written by the finger of God.

Exodus 31:17-18

Now Moses used to take the tent and pitch it outside the camp, far off from the camp, and he called it the Tent of Meeting. So it happened, everyone who sought ADONAI would go out to the Tent of Meeting, which was outside the camp.

Whenever Moses went out to the tent, all the people would arise and stand, everyone at the door of his own tent, and look after Moses, until he had gone into the Tent.

After Moses entered, the pillar of cloud descended, stood at the door, and He would speak with Moses.

When all the people saw the pillar of cloud standing at the entrance of the Tent, they all rose up and worshipped, every man at the entrance of his own tent.

So ADONAI spoke with Moses face to face, as a man speaks with his friend. Then he would return to the camp, but his servant Joshua, the son of Nun, a young man, did not leave the Tent.

So Moses said to ADONAI "You say to me, 'Bring up this people,' but You have not let me know whom You will send with me. Yet You have said, 'I know you by name, and you have also found grace in My eyes.' Now then, I pray, if I have found grace in Your eyes, show me Your ways, so that I may know You, so that I might find favor in Your sight. Consider also that this nation is Your people."

"My presence will go with you, and I will give you rest," He answered.

Exodus 33:7-14

Then he said, "Please, show me Your glory!"

So He said, "I will cause all My goodness to pass before you, and call out the Name of ADONAI before you. I will be gracious toward whom I will be gracious, and I will show mercy on whom I will be merciful."

But He also said, "You cannot see My face, for no man can see Me and live."

Then ADONAI said, "See, a place near Me—you will stand on the rock. While My glory passes by, I will put you in a cleft of the rock, and cover you with My hand, until I have passed by. Then I will take away My hand, and you will see My back, but My face will not be seen."

Exodus 33:18-23

Then ADONAI passed before him, and proclaimed,

"ADONAI, ADONAI, the compassionate and gracious God, slow to anger, and abundant in lovingkindness and truth, showing mercy to a thousand generations, forgiving iniquity and transgression and sin, yet by no means leaving the guilty unpunished, but bringing the iniquity of the fathers upon the children, and upon the children's children, to the third and fourth generation."

Then Moses quickly bowed his head down to the earth and worshipped. He said, "If now I have found grace in Your eyes, my Lord, let my Lord please go within our midst, even though this is a stiff-necked people. Pardon our iniquity and our sin, and take us for Your own inheritance."

Then He said, "I am cutting a covenant. Before all your people I will do wonders, such as have not been done in all the earth, or in any nation. All the people you are among will see the work of ADONAI - for what I am going to do with you will be awesome!

Obey what I am commanding you today. Behold, I am going to drive out the Amorites, Canaanites, Hittites, Perizzites, Hivites and Jebusites before you.
Watch yourself, and make no covenant with the inhabitants of the land where you are going, or they will become a snare among you.
Instead you must break down their altars, smash their pillars and cut down their Asherah poles. For you are to bow down to no other god, because ADONAI is jealous for His Name—He is a jealous God.

Exodus 34:6-14

"You are to keep the Feast of *Matzot*. For seven days you are eat *matzot*, as I commanded you, at the time appointed in the month Aviv, for in the month Aviv you came out from Egypt.

Exodus 34:18

"You are to observe the Feast of *Shavuot*, which is the firstfruits of the wheat harvest, as well as the Feast of Ingathering at the turn of the year. Three times during the year all your males are to appear before ADONAI *Elohim*, God of Israel.

Exodus 34:22-23

Then ADONAI said to Moses, "Write these words, for based on these words I have cut a covenant with you and with Israel."

So he stayed there with ADONAI for 40 days and 40 nights, and he did not eat bread or drink water. He wrote on the tablets the words of the covenant: the Ten Words.

Now it happened, when Moses came down from Mount Sinai with the two tablets of the Testimony in his hand when he came down from the mountain, that Moses did not know that the skin of his face was radiant, because God had spoken with him.

When Aaron and all *Bnei-Yisrael* saw Moses, the skin of his face shone in rays, so they were afraid to come near him. But Moses called out to them, so Aaron and all the rulers of the congregation returned to him, and Moses spoke to them. Afterward all *Bnei-Yisrael* came near, and he gave them all the *mitzvot* that ADONAI had spoken to him in Mount Sinai.

When Moses was done speaking with them, he put a veil over his face. But when Moses went before ADONAI, so that He could speak with him, he took the veil off until he came out.

When he came out and spoke to *Bnei-Yisrael* what he was commanded, *Bnei-Yisrael* saw the face of Moses and that the skin of his face glistened. So Moses put the veil back over his face until he went in to speak with Him.

Exodus 34:27-35

When all the people saw the pillar of cloud standing at the entrance of the Tent, they all rose up and worshiped, every man at the entrance of his own tent.

From Exodus 33:10 TLV ©2018, image #15/54

16. God Disciplines the Scoffers

ADONAI spoke to Moses saying, "Send some men on your behalf to investigate the land of Canaan, which I am giving to *Bnei-Yisrael*. Each man you are to send will be a prince of the tribe of his fathers, a man from each tribe."

So according to the word of ADONAI, Moses sent them from the wilderness of Paran. All the men were princes of *Bnei-Yisrael*.

Numbers 13:1-3

As he sent them to explore the land of Canaan, he said to them, "Go up there through the Negev, then go up into the hill country. See what the land is like and the people living there, whether they might be strong or weak, few or many. In what kind of land are they living? Is it good or bad?

Also, what about the cities in which they are living? Are they unwalled or do they have fortifications? How is the soil—fertile or poor? Are there trees on it or not?

Do your best to bring back some of the fruit of the land." (It was the season for the first ripe grapes.) So they went up and explored the land from the wilderness of Zin as far as Rehob the entrance of Hamath.

Numbers 13:17-21

They returned from investigating the land after 40 days.

They traveled and returned to Moses, Aaron and the entire community of *Bnei-Yisrael* at Kadesh in the wilderness of Paran. They gave their report to them and the entire assembly. They showed the land's fruit.

They gave their account to him and said, "We went into the land where you sent us. Indeed it is flowing with milk and honey—this is some of its fruit.

Numbers 13:25-27

Then Caleb quieted the people before Moses, and said, "We should definitely go up and capture the land, for we can certainly do it!"

But the men who had gone up with him said, "We cannot attack these people, because they are stronger than we."

They spread among *Bnei-Yisrael* a bad report about the land they had explored, saying, "The land through which we passed to explore devours its residents. All the people we saw there are men of great size!

We also saw there the *Nephilim*. (The sons of Anak are from the *Nephilim*.) We seemed like grasshoppers in our eyes as well as theirs!"

Numbers 13:30-33

All through that night, the entire community raised up their voices. The people wept.

All *Bnei-Yisrael* grumbled against Moses and Aaron and the whole community said, "If only we had died in Egypt! If only we had died in this wilderness!

Why is ADONAI bringing us to this land to fall by the sword? Our wives and children will be like plunder! Wouldn't it be better for us to return to Egypt?"

They said to each other, "Let's choose a leader and let's go back to Egypt!"

Then Moses and Aaron fell on their faces before the entire assembly of the community of *Bnei-Yisrael*. Joshua son of Nun and Caleb son of Jephunneh, who were among those who had explored the land, tore their clothes.

They said to the whole assembly of *Bnei-Yisrael*, "The land through which we passed is an exceptionally good land! If ADONAI is pleased with us, He will lead us into that land and will give it to us—a land flowing with milk and honey. Only don't rebel against ADONAI, and don't be afraid of the people of the land. They will be food for us.

The protection over them is gone. ADONAI is with us! Do not fear them."

But the whole assembly talked about violently stoning them.

Then the glory of ADONAI appeared at the Tent of Meeting to all *Bnei-Yisrael*.

ADONAI said to Moses, "How long will these people treat Me contemptibly? How long will they neglect to trust in Me - in spite of all the miraculous signs I have performed among them? ..."

Numbers 14:1-11

"... But as certainly as I live and as certainly as the glory of ADONAI fills the entire earth, none of the people who saw My glory and My miraculous signs I performed in Egypt and in the wilderness - yet tested Me these ten times and did not obey My Voice - not one of them will see the land I promised to their forefathers. None of those who treated Me with contempt will see it!

However, My servant Caleb, because a different spirit is with him and he is wholeheartedly behind Me, I will bring him into the land where he went—his offspring will inherit it. ..."

Numbers 14:21-24

"Not one of you will enter the land about which I lifted My hand to make home for you—except Caleb son of Jephunneh and Joshua son of Nun. ... For 40 years, corresponding to the number of the 40 days you explored the land—one year for each day—you will suffer for your iniquities and know My hostility. I, ADONAI, have spoken and certainly will I do this to all this wicked community banding together against Me. In this wilderness they will meet their end and there they will die!"

Numbers 14:30,34-35

Of those men who had gone to explore the land, only Joshua son of Nun and Caleb son of Jephunneh survived.

Numbers 14:38

ADONAI spoke to Moses saying, "Speak to *Bnei-Yisrael*. Say to them that they are to make for themselves *tzitzit* on the corners of their garments throughout their generations, and they are to put a blue cord on each *tzitzit*. It will be your own *tzitzit*—so whenever you look at them, you will remember all the *mitzvot* of ADONAI and do them and not go spying out after your own hearts and your own eyes, prostituting yourselves.

This way you will remember and obey all My *mitzvot* and you will be holy to your God. I am ADONAI your God. I brought you out of the land of Egypt to be your God. I am ADONAI your God."

Numbers 15:37-41

Then Caleb quieted the people before Moses, and said,
"We should definitely go up and capture the land, for we can certainly do it!"
From Numbers 13:30 TLV ©2018, image #16/54

17. God Keeps Loving His People

"These words ADONAI spoke to all your assembly on the mountain from the midst of the fire, the cloud and the fog, with a great voice. He added no more. He wrote them on two tablets of stone and gave them to me.

"As soon as you heard the voice from the midst of the darkness, while the mountain was blazing with fire, you came near to me—all the heads of your tribes and your elders.

Then you said,

'ADONAI our God has just shown us His glory and His greatness, and we have heard His voice from the midst of the fire. This day we have seen that God speaks with man, and yet he keeps on living. Now then, why should we die? For this great fire will consume us! If we hear the voice of ADONAI our God any more, then we will die.

For who is there of all flesh who has heard the voice of the living God speaking from the midst of the fire, as we have, and lived? You go near and hear all that ADONAI our God says. Then you tell us all what ADONAI our God tells you, and we will hear it and do it.'

"ADONAI heard the tone of your words when you spoke to me, and ADONAI said to me,

'I have heard the tone of the words that this people has spoken to you—they have done well in all they have spoken. If only there were such a heart in them to fear Me and keep all My mitzvot always, so that it might go well with them and with their children forever!

Go say to them, "Return to your tents." But as for you, stand here by Me, and I will tell you the whole commandment—both the statutes and the ordinances that you are to teach them. And they will do them in the land I am giving them to possess.'

Deuteronomy 5:19-28

"Now this is the commandment, the statutes and ordinances that ADONAI your God commanded to teach you to do in the land you are crossing over to possess - so that you might fear ADONAI your God, to keep all His statutes and mitzvot that I am commanding you and your son and your son's son all the days of your life, and so that you may prolong your days.

Hear, therefore, O Israel, and take care to do this, so that it may go well with you and you may increase mightily, as ADONAI the God of your fathers has promised you, in a land flowing with milk and honey.

"Hear O Israel, the LORD our God, the LORD is one. Love ADONAI your God with all your heart and with all your soul and with all your strength. These words, which I am commanding you today, are to be on your heart. You are to teach them diligently to your children, and speak of them when you sit in your house, when you walk by the way, when you lie down and when you rise up. Bind them as a sign on your hand, they are to be as frontlets between your eyes, and write them on the doorposts of your house and on your gates.

Deuteronomy 6:1-9

"When your son asks you in time to come, saying 'What are the testimonies and the statutes and the ordinances that ADONAI our God commanded you?' then you are to tell your son, 'We were slaves to Pharaoh in Egypt, and ADONAI brought us out from Egypt with a mighty hand.

Before our eyes ADONAI showed signs and wonders, great and terrible—on Egypt, on Pharaoh, and on all his house. Then He brought us out from there so that He might bring us in, to give us the land that He swore to our fathers.

ADONAI commanded us to do all these statutes, to fear ADONAI our God—for our good always, to keep us alive, as is the case this day. It will be righteousness to us, if we take care to do all this commandment before ADONAI our God, just as He has commanded us.'

Deuteronomy 6:20-25

"It is not because you are more numerous than all the peoples that ADONAI set His love on you and chose you—for you are the least of all peoples.

Rather, because of His love for you and His keeping the oath He swore to your fathers, ADONAI brought you out with a mighty hand and redeemed you from the house of slavery, from the hand of Pharaoh king of Egypt.

Deuteronomy 7:7-8

"Then it will happen, as a result of your listening to these ordinances, when you keep and do them, that ADONAI your God will keep with you the covenant kindness that He swore to your fathers. He will love you, bless you and multiply you. ..."

Deuteronomy 7:12-13a

ADONAI will remove all sickness from you, and He will not inflict on you any of the terrible diseases of Egypt that you knew, but will inflict them on all who hate you.

Deuteronomy 7:15

"You are to take care to do the whole *mitzvah* that I am commanding you today, so that you may live and multiply and go in and possess the land that ADONAI swore to your fathers.

You are to remember all the way that ADONAI your God has led you these 40 years in the wilderness—in order to humble you, to test you, to know what was in your heart, whether you would keep His *mitzvot* or not.

He afflicted you and let you hunger, then He fed you *manna*—which neither you nor your fathers had known—in order to make you understand that man does not live by bread alone but by every word that comes from the mouth of ADONAI.

Neither did your clothing wear out on you, nor did your foot swell these 40 years. Now you know in your heart that as a man disciplines his son, so ADONAI your God disciplines you. So you are to keep the *mitzvot* of ADONAI your God—to walk in His ways and to fear Him.

For ADONAI your God is bringing you into a good land—a land of wadis with water, of springs and fountains flowing out in the valleys and hills, a land of wheat and barley, vines, figs and pomegranates, a land of olive oil and honey, a land where you will eat bread with no poverty, where you will lack nothing, a land whose stones are iron, and out of whose hills you can dig copper.

So you will eat and be full, and you will bless ADONAI your God for the good land He has given you.

"Take care that you do not forget ADONAI your God by not keeping His *mitzvot*, ordinances and statutes that I am commanding you today.

Deuteronomy 8:1-11

Hear O Israel, the LORD our God, the LORD is one.
Love ADONAI your God with all your heart and with all your soul and with all your strength.
From Deuteronomy 6:4-5 TLV ©2018, image #17/54

18. God Answers their Shout

Now Joshua son of Nun was full of the spirit of wisdom, for Moses had laid his hands on him. So *Bnei-Yisrael* listened to him and did just as ADONAI had commanded Moses.

Deuteronomy 34:9

Now it came about after the death of Moses the servant of ADONAI that ADONAI spoke to Joshua son of Nun, Moses' aide saying:

"My servant Moses is dead. So now, arise, you and all these people, cross over this Jordan to the land that I am giving to them— to *Bnei-Yisrael*. Every place on which the sole of your foot treads, I am giving to you, as I spoke to Moses. From the wilderness and this Lebanon to the great river, the Euphrates River—all the land of the Hittites—to the Great Sea toward the setting of the sun will be your territory.

No one will be able to stand before you all the days of your life. Just as I was with Moses, so I will be with you. I will not fail you or forsake you.

Chazak! Be strong! For you will lead these people to inherit the land I swore to their fathers to give them.

Only be very strong, and resolute to observe diligently the *Torah* which Moses, My servant commanded you. Do not turn from it to the right or to the left, so you may be successful wherever you go.

This book of the *Torah* should not depart from your mouth—you are to meditate on it day and night, so that you may be careful to do everything written in it. For then you will make your ways prosperous and then you will be successful.

Have I not commanded you? *Chazak*! Be strong! Do not be terrified or dismayed, for ADONAI your God is with you wherever you go."

Joshua 1:1-9

Then Joshua son of Nun secretly sent out two spies from Shittim saying: "Go, explore the land, especially Jericho."

Joshua 2:1

Then Joshua told the people, "Consecrate yourselves, for tomorrow ADONAI will do wonders in your midst."

Joshua spoke to the *kohanim* saying: "Take up the ark of the covenant and cross over ahead of the people." So they took up the ark of the covenant and went ahead of the people.

Now ADONAI said to Joshua, "This day I will begin to exalt you in the eyes of all Israel, so they may know that just as I was with Moses, so I will be with you.

You are to command the *kohanim* who are carrying the ark of the covenant saying:

'When you reach the edge of the waters of the Jordan, you are to stand still in the Jordan.'"

Joshua 3:5-8

It will come to pass when the soles of the feet of the *kohanim* who are carrying the ark of ADONAI, Sovereign of all the earth, rest in the waters of the Jordan, the Jordan's waters will be cut off. The waters coming downstream will stand up in one heap." So it came to pass. ...

Joshua 3:13-14a

So the people crossed over opposite Jericho. Yet the *kohanim* carrying the ark of the covenant of ADONAI stood firmly on dry ground in the middle of the Jordan, while all Israel crossed over on dry ground, until the entire nation had finished crossing over the Jordan.

Joshua 3:16c-17

On that day ADONAI exalted Joshua in the eyes of all Israel. So they revered him, just as they had revered Moses all the days of his life.

Joshua 4:14

Now Jericho was tightly shut up because of *Bnei-Yisrael*—no one going out and no one coming in.

Then ADONAI said to Joshua, "Look, I have given Jericho into your hand, with its king and mighty warriors. Now you are to march around the city, all the men of war circling the city once. So you are to do for six days. Seven *kohanim* will carry seven *shofarot* of rams' horns before the ark.

Then on the seventh day you are to circle the city seven times while the *kohanim* blow the *shofarot*. It will be when they make a long blast with the ram's horn, when you hear the sound of the *shofar*, have all the people shout a loud shout—then the wall of the city will fall down flat, and the people will go up, everyone straight ahead."

So Joshua son of Nun summoned the *kohanim* and said to them, "Take up the ark of the covenant. Let seven *kohanim* carry seven *shofarot* of rams' horns before the ark of ADONAI."

Then he said to the people, "Move forward, march around the city, and let the armed force march ahead of the ark of ADONAI."
And it was so. …

Joshua 6:1-8a

But Joshua ordered the people saying: "You must not shout nor let your voice be heard nor let a word proceed out of your mouth, until the day I tell you 'shout!' Then you will shout."

So he had the ark of ADONAI go around the city, circling it once. Then they came into the camp and spent the night there.

The next day Joshua rose early in the morning. The *kohanim* took up the ark of ADONAI, and the seven *kohanim* carrying the seven *shofarot* of rams' horns marched in front of the ark of ADONAI and blew the *shofarot*, with the armed force marching before them and the rear guard marching behind the ark of ADONAI, while the *shofarot* continued to blow. So the second day they circled the city once and returned to the camp. So they did for six days.

Now on the seventh day they rose early, at dawn, and marched around the city in the same way seven times. Only on that day did they march around the city seven times.

Then on the seventh time, when the *kohanim* blew the *shofarot*, Joshua ordered the people, "Shout! For ADONAI has given you the city! …"

Joshua 6:10   -16

So when the *shofarot* blew, the people shouted. When the people heard the sound of the *shofar*, the people shouted a loud shout— and the wall fell down flat! So the people went up into the city, everyone straight ahead, and they captured the city.

Joshua 6:20

So ADONAI was with Joshua, and his fame was throughout the region.

Joshua 6:27

Then ADONAI said to Joshua, "Look, I have given Jericho into your hand, with its king and mighty warriors. Now you are to march around the city, all the men of war circling the city once. So you are to do for six days.

From Joshua 6:1-2 TLV ©2018, image #18/54

19. God Fights the Battle

Now when Joshua had sent the people away, *Bnei-Yisrael* went every man to his inheritance to possess the land. Then the people worshipped ADONAI all the days of Joshua, and all the days of the elders that outlived Joshua, who had seen all the great work of ADONAI that He had done for Israel.

Then Joshua son of Nun, the servant of ADONAI, died at the age of 110 years, and they buried him in the territory of his inheritance in Timnath-heres, in the hill country of Ephraim north of Mount Gaash.

But when all that generation were gathered to their fathers, there arose another generation after them that did not experience ADONAI or the work that He had done for Israel.

Judges 2:6-10

Then ADONAI raised up judges who delivered them from the hand of those who plundered them.

Judges 2:16

Whenever ADONAI raised judges up for them, ADONAI was with the judge and delivered them from the hand of their enemies all the days of the judge. For ADONAI was moved to pity by their groaning because of those who oppressed and crushed them.

But when the judge died, they would keep turning back and acted more corruptly than their fathers, in following other gods, worshipping them, and bowing down to them. They abandoned none of their practices and stubborn ways.

Judges 2:18-19

Now Deborah, a woman who was a prophetess, the wife of Lappidoth, was judging Israel at that time.

She used to sit under the palm tree of Deborah between Ramah and Bethel in the hill country of Ephraim, and *Bnei-Yisrael* came up to her for judgment.

Now she sent and summoned Barak son of Abinoam from Kedesh in Naphtali, and said to him, "Hasn't ADONAI, God of Israel, commanded, 'Go, march to Mount Tabor, and take with you 10,000 men of the sons of Naphtali and of the sons of Zebulun? Then at the Kishon torrent, I will draw out to you Sisera, commander of Jabin's army with his chariots and his multitude, and I will give him into your hand.'"

But Barak said to her, "If you are going with me, then I will go. But if you aren't going with me, I won't go."

"Surely I will go with you," she said. "However, no honor will be yours on the way that you are about to go—for ADONAI will sell Sisera into the hand of a woman."

So Deborah arose and went with Barak to Kedesh. Then Barak summoned Zebulun and Naphtali together to Kedesh, and 10,000 men marched up after him, and Deborah went up with him.

Judges 4:4-10

Then Deborah said to Barak, "Arise! For this is the day in which ADONAI will deliver Sisera into your hand. Has ADONAI not gone out before you?"

So Barak came down from Mount Tabor with 10,000 men following him. ADONAI threw Sisera and all his chariots and all his army into confusion before Barak with the edge of the sword.

Then Sisera got down from his chariot and fled away on foot. But Barak pursued the chariots and the army as far as Harosheth-ha-goyim. The whole army of Sisera fell by the sword; not one was left.

Judges 4:14-16

Then Yael, Heber's wife, took a tent pin and got a hammer in her hand, approached him stealthily and drove the pin into his temple until it pierced through into the ground—for he was exhausted and in a deep sleep. So he died.

Now behold, as Barak was pursuing Sisera, Yael came out to meet him and said to him, "Come, I will show you the man whom you are seeking." So he entered with her, and behold, Sisera was lying dead, with a tent-pin in his temple! So on that day God subdued King Jabin of Canaan before *Bnei-Yisrael*.

Judges 4:21-23

Then Deborah and Barak son of Abinoam sang on that day saying:

"When leaders take the lead in Israel,
when people freely offer themselves,
 bless *ADONAI*!
Listen, O kings! Give ear, O rulers!
I, to *ADONAI* I will sing,
I will sing praise to *ADONAI*,
 the God of Israel.
ADONAI, when You came out from Seir,
when You marched from Edom's field,
 the earth trembled,
 the heavens also dropped,
 yes, the clouds dropped water.
The mountains quaked before *ADONAI*,
this Sinai at the presence of *ADONAI*,
 the God of Israel!

In the days of Shamgar son of Anath,
 in the days of Yael,
the highways were deserted,
 travelers walked by crooked paths.
Villages were deserted in Israel,
 deserted, until I, Deborah, arose,
 a mother in Israel arose.
They chose new gods—
 then war was in the gates.
No shield or spear was seen
 among 40,000 in Israel!
My heart is with Israel's rulers,
who offer themselves freely among the people.
Bless *ADONAI*!
Riders on white donkeys,
sitting on saddle blankets,
traveling on the road, sing!
Louder than the sound of archers,
 at the watering places!
There let them rehearse
 the righteous acts of *ADONAI*,
 the righteous deeds for His villages in Israel.
Then the people of *ADONAI*
 went down to the gates.
Awake, awake, Deborah!
Awake, awake, utter a song!
Arise, Barak, lead away your captives,
O son of Abinoam!

Judges 5:1-12

... So let all Your enemies perish, *ADONAI*!
 But may those who love Him
 be like the rising of the sun in its might."

Then the land had peace for 40 years.

Judges 5:31

Now Deborah, a woman who was a prophetess, the wife of Lappidoth, was judging Israel at that time. S he used to sit under the palm tree of Deborah between Ramah and Bethel in the hill country of Ephraim, and *Bnei-Yisrael* came up to her for judgment.
From Judges 4:4-5 TLV ©2018, image #19/54

20. God Grants her Prayers

Now there was a certain man of Ramathaim-zophim, of the hill country of Ephraim—his name was Elkanah son of Jeroham son of Elihu son of Tohu son of Zuph, an Ephraimite.

1 Samuel 1:1

Now this man used to go up from his town every year to worship and to sacrifice to *Adonai-Tzva'ot* in Shiloh. ...

1 Samuel 1:3a

Then on the designated day Elkanah would sacrifice and give portions to his wife Peninnah and to all her sons and daughters, but to Hannah he would give only one portion—even though he loved Hannah—for *Adonai* had closed her womb.

Her rival would taunt her bitterly to provoke her, because *Adonai* had closed her womb. So it was year after year, whenever she went up to the House of *Adonai*, that she would provoke her; so she wept and would not eat.

1 Samuel 1:4-7

... Now Eli the *kohen* was sitting on his seat by the doorpost of the Temple of *Adonai*. While her soul was bitter, she prayed to *Adonai* and wept.

So she made a vow and said, "*Adonai-Tzva'ot*, if You will indeed look upon the affliction of Your handmaid, remember me and not forget Your handmaid, but grant Your handmaid a son, then I will give him to *Adonai* all the days of his life and no razor will ever touch his head."

It came to pass, as she prayed long before *Adonai*, that Eli was watching her mouth. Now Hannah was praying in her heart - only her lips were moving, but her voice could not be heard. So Eli thought she was drunk. Then Eli said to her, "How long will you be drunk? Get rid of your wine!"

But in response Hannah said, "No, my lord, I am a woman with an oppressed spirit! I haven't been drinking wine or beer. Instead I've been pouring out my soul before *Adonai*. Don't consider your handmaid a wicked woman. For out of my great anguish and grief I've been praying until now."

Then Eli responded, "Go in *shalom*, and may the God of Israel grant your petition that you asked of Him."

"May your maidservant find favor in your eyes," she said. So the woman went her way; she ate, and her countenance was no longer dejected.

1 Samuel 1:9b-18

So it came to pass at the turn of the year that Hannah conceived and gave birth to a son. She called his name Samuel, "because I have asked *Adonai* for him."

1 Samuel 1:20

When she had weaned him, she took him up with her, along with three bulls, one ephah of flour and a jar of wine, and brought him to the House of *Adonai* in Shiloh, while the child was still young.

After they slaughtered the bull, they brought the boy to Eli. "It's me, my lord!" she said. "As your soul lives, my lord, I am the woman that stood by you here, praying to *Adonai*. For this boy I prayed, and *Adonai* has granted me my petition that I asked of Him. So I in turn dedicate him to *Adonai* — as long as he lives he is dedicated to *Adonai*."

Then he bowed in worship there before *Adonai*.

1 Samuel 1:24-28

Then Hannah prayed and said,

"My heart exults in *Adonai*,

my horn is lifted high in *Adonai*.

I smile wide over my enemies,

for I rejoice in Your salvation.

There is none holy as *Adonai*,

for there is none besides You,

nor is there any rock like our God.

Boast no more so proudly—

insolence comes out of your mouth.

For *Adonai* is the all-knowing God,

and by Him deeds are weighed.

The bows of the mighty are broken,

but the stumbling are girded with strength.

Those full hire themselves for bread,

but those starving hunger no more.

Even the barren gives birth to seven,

but she with many sons languishes.

Adonai causes death and makes alive,

He brings down to *Sheol* and raises up.

Adonai makes poor and makes rich,

He brings low and also lifts up.

He raises the helpless from the dust.

1 Samuel 2:1-8a

Now the boy Samuel was in the service of *Adonai* under Eli. In those days the word of *Adonai* was rare—there were no visions breaking through.

One day, Eli was lying down in his place—now his eyes had grown dim so that he could not see, and the lamp of God had not yet gone out. Samuel was lying down in *Adonai's* Temple, where the ark of God was.

Then *Adonai* called, "Samuel!" So he answered, "Here I am." Then he ran to Eli and said, "Here I am, for you called me."

But he replied, "I didn't call—go back to sleep." So he went back and lay down.

Then *Adonai* called Samuel yet again. So Samuel arose and went to Eli, and said, "Here I am, for you called me."

But he answered, "I didn't call, my son—go back to sleep." Now Samuel had not experienced *Adonai* yet, since the word of *Adonai* had not yet been revealed to him.

Adonai called Samuel again for the third time. So he got up and went to Eli, and said "Here I am, for you called me."

Then Eli perceived that *Adonai* was calling the boy. So Eli said to Samuel, "Go back to sleep, and if He calls you, say: 'Speak, *Adonai*, for Your servant is listening.'"

So Samuel went back and lay down in his place. Then *Adonai* came and stood and called as at the other times, "Samuel! Samuel!"

Then Samuel said, "Speak, for Your servant is listening."

1 Samuel 3:1-10

So Samuel grew up and *Adonai* was with him, and let none of his words fall to the ground.

Then all Israel from Dan to Beersheba knew that Samuel was entrusted as a prophet of *Adonai*. *Adonai* started to appear once more in Shiloh, for *Adonai* revealed Himself to Samuel in Shiloh by the word of *Adonai*.

1 Samuel 3:19-21

"It's me, my lord!" she said. "As your soul lives, my lord, I am the woman that stood by you here, praying to ADONAI.
For this boy I prayed, and ADONAI has granted me my petition that I asked of Him.
So I in turn dedicate him to ADONAI — as long as he lives he is dedicated to ADONAI."
From 1 Samuel 1:26-28 TLV ©2018, image #20/54

21. God Anoints a King

Now ADONAI said to Samuel, "How long will you grieve over Saul, since I have rejected him as king over Israel? Fill your horn with oil and go. I am sending you to Jesse the Bethlehemite, for I have selected for Myself a king among his sons."

1 Samuel 16:1

So Samuel did what ADONAI said and went to Beth-lehem.

1 Samuel 16:4a

Thus Jesse made seven of his sons pass before Samuel. But Samuel said to Jesse, "ADONAI has not chosen any of these."

Then Samuel asked Jesse, "Are these all the boys you have?"

"There's still the youngest," he replied. But right now, he's tending the sheep."

"Send and bring him," Samuel said to Jesse, "for we will not sit down until he comes here." So he sent word and had him come. Now he was ruddy-cheeked, with beautiful eyes and a handsome appearance.

Then ADONAI said, "Arise, anoint him, for this is the one." So Samuel took the horn of oil and anointed him in the midst of his brothers. From that day on *Ruach ADONAI* came mightily upon David.

1 Samuel 16:10-13b

Now the Philistines assembled their armies to battle.

1 Samuel 17:1a

Then a champion stepped out from the camp of the Philistines, named Goliath, from Gath, whose height was six cubits and a span.

1 Samuel 17:4

Then he stood and shouted out to the ranks of Israel saying to them, "Why come out to line up in battle array? Am I not the Philistine and aren't you Saul's servants? Choose for yourselves a man and let him come down to me. If he is able to fight with me and kill me, then will we become your slaves; but if I prevail against him and kill him, then will you become our slaves and serve us."

The Philistine added, "Today I defy the ranks of Israel—give me a man, so we may fight together!" But when Saul and all Israel heard these words of the Philistine, they were dismayed and very terrified.

1 Samuel 17:8-11

David said to Saul, "Let no one's heart fail because of him. Your servant will go and fight with this Philistine."

1 Samuel 17:32

Then he took his staff in his hand, chose five smooth stones from the valley, put them in the pocket of the shepherd's bag that he had, and with his sling in his hand, he approached the Philistine.

1 Samuel 17:40

Then David said to the Philistine, "You are coming to me with a sword, a spear and a javelin, but I am coming to you in the Name of ADONAI-Tzva'ot, God of the armies of Israel, whom you have defied."

1 Samuel 17:45

Then when the Philistine rose and began to advance, drawing near to meet David, David ran quickly toward the battle line to meet the Philistine. David put his hand in his bag, took from it a stone and slung it, striking the Philistine on his forehead.

The stone sank into his forehead, so that he fell on his face to the ground.

So David prevailed over the Philistine with a sling and a stone, struck the Philistine down and killed him.

1 Samuel 17:48-50a

Now Saul became afraid of David, because *ADONAI* was with him but had departed from Saul. Therefore Saul removed him from his entourage by appointing him as a captain of a thousand. So David went out and came in before the troops. David had success in all his undertakings, since *ADONAI* was with him.

When Saul saw that he had great success, he dreaded him. But all Israel and Judah loved David, for he went out and came in before them.

1 Samuel 18:12-16

Now the Philistines were fighting against Israel. Israel's men fled before the Philistines and many fell slain on Mount Gilboa.

1 Samuel 31:1

So Saul, his three sons, his armor-bearer, and all his men died together that same day.

1 Samuel 31:6

Then all the tribes of Israel came to David at Hebron and spoke saying, "Here we are, your own flesh and blood. Even before, when Saul was king over us, it was you who led Israel out and back. Also, *ADONAI* said to you, 'You will shepherd My people Israel and be ruler over Israel.'"

So all the elders of Israel came to Hebron, and King David cut a covenant with them at Hebron before *ADONAI*. Then they anointed David king over Israel.

2 Samuel 5:1-3

Now the king and his soldiers marched to Jerusalem against the Jebusites, the inhabitants of the region.

2 Samuel 5:6a

So David occupied the stronghold and renamed it the City of David. Then David fortified it all round from the Millo inward. David continued to grow stronger, for *ADONAI Elohim-Tzva'ot* was with him.

Then King Hiram of Tyre sent envoys to David with cedar logs, carpenters and masons; and they built a palace for David.

David then realized that *ADONAI* had established him as king over Israel, and that He had exalted his kingdom for the sake of His people Israel.

2 Samuel 5:9-12

Now David again gathered all the chosen men of Israel, 30,000. Then David and all the people who were with him arose and set out from Baale-judah to bring up from there the ark of God, which is called by the Name, the very Name of *ADONAI-Tzva'ot* who is enthroned between the *cheruvim*.

2 Samuel 6:1-2

Now it came about when the king lived in his palace and *ADONAI* had granted him rest from all his enemies around him, that the king said to the prophet Nathan, "See now, I am living in a house of cedar, yet the ark of God remains within curtains."

"Go, do all that is in your heart," Nathan said to the king, "for *ADONAI* is with you."

But it came to pass the same night that the word of *ADONAI* came to Nathan saying: "Go, tell My servant David:

Thus says *ADONAI*: Are you to build Me a house for Me to dwell in? ..."

2 Samuel 7:1-5

"Moreover, *ADONAI* declares to you that *ADONAI* will make a house for you. When your days are done and you sleep with your fathers, I will raise up your seed, who will come forth from you after you, and I will establish his kingdom.

He will build a house for My Name, and I will establish his royal throne forever. I will be a father to him, and he will be a son to Me. ..."

2 Samuel 7:11c-14a

So David prevailed over the Philistine with a sling and a stone, struck the Philistine down and killed him.

From 1 Samuel 17:50 TLV ©2018, image #21/54

87

22. God Sends a Prophet

Now Elijah the Tishbite, one of the settlers of Gilead, said to Ahab: "As ADONAI God of Israel lives, before whom I stand, there shall be no dew or rain these years, except at my word."

Then the word of ADONAI came to him saying: "Leave this place, turn eastward, and hide yourself by the Wadi Cherith, east of the Jordan. It will come about that you will drink from the wadi. I have also commanded the ravens to feed you there."

So he went and did according to the word of ADONAI —he went and lived by the Wadi Cherith, which is east of the Jordan. The ravens kept bringing him bread and meat in the morning and bread and meat in the evening, and he drank from the wadi.

1 Kings 17:1-6

So Ahab sent word to all the children of Israel and gathered all the prophets together at Mount Carmel.

Then Elijah approached all the people and said, "How long will you waver between two opinions? If ADONAI is God, then follow Him; but if Baal is, follow him." But the people did not answer him, not even a word.

Then Elijah said to the people, "I am the only prophet of ADONAI left, but Baal's prophets are 450 men. Now let them give us two young bulls. Let them choose one bull for themselves, cut it into pieces, lay it on the wood, and put no fire underneath, while I prepare the other bull, lay it on the wood, and put no fire underneath.

Then you will call on the name of your god, and then, I will call on the Name of ADONAI. The God who answers with fire, He is God."

All the people responded and said, "It's a good thing."

1 Kings 18:20-24

When midday was past, they kept prophesying ecstatically until the time of offering up the evening sacrifice. But there was no voice, no one answering, no one paying attention.

Then Elijah said to all the people, "Come near to me." So all the people came closer to him. Then he repaired the damaged altar of ADONAI.

1 Kings 18:29-30

Now it was at the time of offering up the evening sacrifice that Elijah the prophet came near and said, "ADONAI, God of Abraham, Isaac and Israel, let it be known today that You are God in Israel, that I am Your servant, and that I have done all these things at Your word.

Answer me, ADONAI, answer me, so that these people may know that You, ADONAI, are God, and that You have turned their heart back again."

Then the fire of ADONAI fell and consumed the burnt offering—and the wood, the stones and the dust—and licked up the water that was in the trench. When all the people saw it, they fell on their faces, and they said, "ADONAI, He is God! ADONAI, He is God!"

1 Kings 18:36-39

Then Elijah said to Ahab, "Go up, eat and drink, for there's the sound of rain." So Ahab went up to eat and drink. But Elijah went up to the top of Carmel, crouched on the ground and put his face between his knees.

Then he said to his servant, "Go up now, look toward the sea." So he went up, looked, and said, "There's nothing." Then he said, "Go back" - seven times - and it was the seventh time that he said, "Look! A cloud as small as a man's hand is rising from the sea."

1 Kings 18:41-44a

… In a little while the sky grew black with clouds and wind, and there was a heavy rain.

1 Kings 18:45a

Then the angel of ADONAI came again a second time, touched him and said. "Get up and eat, because the journey is too much for you."

So he arose and ate and drank, and in the strength of that meal forty days and forty nights went to Horeb, the mountain of God.

Then He said, "Come out and stand on the mount before ADONAI." Behold, ADONAI was passing by—a great and mighty wind was tearing at the mountains and shattering cliffs before ADONAI.

But ADONAI was not in the wind. After the wind there was an earthquake, but ADONAI was not in the earthquake. After the earthquake a fire, but ADONAI was not in the fire. After the fire there was a soft whisper of a voice.

As soon as Elijah heard it, he wrapped his face in his mantle, went out and stood at the entrance of the cave. Then all of a sudden, a voice addressed him and said, "What are you doing here, Elijah?"

1 Kings 19:11-13

Then ADONAI said to him, "Go, return on your way to the wilderness of Damascus, and when you get there, anoint Hazael king over Aram, and anoint Jehu son of Nimshi king over Israel, and anoint Elisha son of Shaphat of Abel-meholah as prophet in your place.

1 Kings 19:15-16

So he departed from there and found Elisha son of Shaphat while he was plowing with twelve pairs of oxen before him, and he with the twelfth. Then Elijah crossed over to him and threw his mantle on him.

1 Kings 19:19

Now it came to pass, when ADONAI was about to take up Elijah by a whirlwind into heaven, that Elijah went with Elisha from Gilgal. Elijah said to Elisha, "Stay here please, for ADONAI has sent me on to Bethel."

But Elisha said, "As ADONAI lives, and as you live, I will not leave you." So they went down to Bethel.

2 Kings 2:1-2

Now as they were crossing over, Elijah said to Elisha, "Ask what I will do for you before I am taken from you."

So Elisha said, "Please, let a double portion of your spirit be upon me."

He replied, "You have asked a hard thing. Nevertheless, if you see me when I am taken from you, it will be so to you; but if not, it will not be so."

As they were walking along and talking, behold, a chariot of fire and horses of fire separated the two of them, and Elijah went up by a whirlwind into heaven.

As Elisha was watching, he was crying out, "Avi! Avi! The chariot of Israel and its horsemen!"

Then he saw him no more. So he took hold of his own clothes and tore them in two pieces. He then picked up the mantle of Elijah that fell from him.

2 Kings 2:9-13a

90

As they were walking along and talking, behold, a chariot of fire and horses of fire separated the two of them, and Elijah went up by a whirlwind into heaven.

From 2 Kings 2:11 TLV ©2018, image #22/54

He then picked up the mantle of Elijah that fell from him. When he returned and stood by the bank of the Jordan, he took the mantle of Elijah that had fallen off him, struck the waters and said, "Where is ADONAI, the God of Elijah?" As he indeed struck the waters, they parted here then there. Then Elisha crossed over.

When the sons of the prophets at Jericho saw him some way off, they said, "The spirit of Elijah has rested on Elisha." So they came to meet him and bowed down to the ground before him.

2 Kings 2:13-15

Then the men of the city said to Elisha, "Look now, the situation of this city is pleasant, as my lord sees, but the water is bad and the land barren."

He responded, "Bring me a new jar, and put salt in it." So they brought it to him. Then he went out to the spring of water, threw salt in it and said, "Thus says ADONAI, I have healed this water. No longer will there be from there death or barrenness." So the waters were healed to this day, according to the word that Elisha spoke.

2 Kings 2:19-22

Now a certain woman of the wives of the sons of the prophets cried out to Elisha saying, "Your servant my husband is dead—you know that your servant feared ADONAI. Now the creditor has come to take my two children to be his slaves."

"What should I do for you?" Elisha asked her. "Tell me, what do you have in the house?" She replied, "Your handmaid has nothing in the house except a jar of oil." Then he said, "Go borrow for yourself vessels from all your neighbors—empty jars—not just a few. Then go inside and shut the door behind you and behind your sons, and pour into all those vessels, setting aside what is full."

So she left him and shut the door behind her and behind her sons. They kept bringing the vessels to her and she kept pouring. When the vessels were full, she said to her son, "Bring me another vessel." But he said to her, "There isn't another vessel." So the oil stopped. Then she came and told the man of God. So he said, "Go sell the oil and pay your debt, then you and your sons can live on the rest.

One day when Elisha passed through Shunem, where there was a prominent woman who persuaded him to eat some food. And so it was, whenever he passed through, he would stop for a meal. Then she said to her husband, "Behold now, I realize that this man who often passes through is a holy man of God. Please, let's make a little walled room on the roof, and let's put there a bed, a table, a chair, and a lampstand for him. Then whenever he comes to us, he can stay there."

One day he came there, and retired to the upper chamber and lay down there. Then he said to Gehazi his servant, "Call this Shunammite woman." When he had called her, she stood before him. He said to him, "Tell her: Behold, you have gone to all this trouble for us. What can be done for you? ..."

2 Kings 4:1-13b

Then he said, "At this season next year, you will be embracing a son." But she said, "No, my lord, do not lie to your handmaid, man of God." Nevertheless, the woman conceived and bore a son during that season the following year, just as Elisha had told her. Now when the child was grown, one day he went out to his father among the reapers. Then he said to his father, "My head, my head!" So he said to his servant, "Carry him to his mother." So he picked him up and brought him to his mother. The child sat on her lap until noon, and then died. She then went up and laid him on the bed of the man of God, shut the door on him and went out. Then she called to her husband, and said, "Please send me one of the servants and one of the donkeys that I may run to the man of God and come back."

But he said, "Why are you going to him today? It is neither New Moon or nor *Shabbat*."

But she said, "It will be well."

2 Kings 4:16-23

When Elisha entered the house, there was the child, dead and laying on his bed. So he entered and shut the door behind the two of them and prayed to ADONAI.

2 Kings 4:32-33

The child sneezed seven times, then the child opened his eyes. He then called Gehazi and said, "Call the Shunammite." So he called her. When she came in to him, he said, "Pick up your son." She came, fell at his feet and bowed down to the ground. Then she picked up her son and went out.

2 Kings 4:35b-37

Now a man came from Baal-shalishah, and brought the man of God bread of the firstfruits—20 loaves of barley bread and fresh ears of corn in his sack. Then he said, "Give them to the people that they may eat." But his attendant said, "What? Will I set this before a hundred men?" But he said, "Give them to the people that they may eat, for thus says ADONAI, 'They will eat and will have left over.'" So he set it before them, and they ate and had some left over, according to the word of ADONAI.

2 Kings 4:42-44

Now the sons of the prophets said to Elisha, "Behold now, the place where we are living in your presence is too cramped for us.

2 Kings 6:1

So he went with them. And when they came to the Jordan, they began to cut down trees. But as one of them was cutting down a beam, the axe-head fell into the water; and he cried, and said, "Ah, my master! It was borrowed." Then the man of God asked, Where did it fall?"

When he showed him the place, he cut off a stick and threw it there, and made the ax head float. Then he said, "Pick it up for yourself." So he reached out his hand and took it.

2 Kings 6:4-7

Now the king of Aram was warring against Israel.

2 Kings 6:8a

Now when the attendant of the man of God had risen early and gone out, behold, an army with horses and chariots was surrounding the city. So his attendant said to him, "Alas, my master! What are we going to do?"

"Fear not," he replied, "for those who are with us are more than those who are with them." Then Elisha prayed and said, "ADONAI, please open his eyes that he may see." Then ADONAI opened the eyes of the young man and he saw, and behold, the mountain was full of horses and chariots of fire all around Elisha.

2 Kings 6:15-17

Then Elisha died, and they buried him. Now bands of Moabite marauders used to invade the land at the spring of the year. It came about, as they were burying a man, behold, they saw a marauding band, so they threw the man's body into Elisha's tomb. As soon as the man's body touched Elisha's bones, he came back to life and stood up on his feet!

2 Kings 13:20-21

So she left him and shut the door behind her and behind her sons. They kept bringing the vessels to her and she kept pouring. When the vessels were full, she said to her son, "Bring me another vessel."

From 2 Kings 4:5-6 TLV ©2018, image #23/54

24. God Proclaims His Promise

The words of Jeremiah son of Hilkiah, one of the *kohanim* who were in Anathoth in the land of Benjamin. The word of ADONAI came to him during the days of King Josiah of Judah, son of Amon, in the thirteenth year of his reign.

Jeremiah 1:1-2

The word of ADONAI came to me, saying: "Before I formed you in the womb, I knew you, and before you were born, I set you apart - I appointed you prophet to the nations."

Jeremiah 1:4-5

Then ADONAI stretched out His hand and touched my mouth and ADONAI said to me, "Behold, I have put My words in your mouth. See, today I have appointed you over nations and over kingdoms: to uproot and to tear down, to destroy and to overthrow, to build and to plant."

Moreover, the word of ADONAI came to me, saying, "What do you see, Jeremiah?" I answered, "I see an almond branch." Then ADONAI said to me, "You have seen correctly, for I am watching over My word to perform it."

Jeremiah 1:9-12

Blessed is the one who trusts in ADONAI, whose confidence is in ADONAI. For he will be like a tree planted by the waters, spreading out its roots by a stream. It has no fear when heat comes, but its leaves will be green. It does not worry in a year of drought, nor depart from yielding fruit.

Jeremiah 17:7-8

ADONAI showed me, all of a sudden, there were two baskets of figs set before the Temple of ADONAI.

Jeremiah 24:1a

One basket had very good figs, like the figs that are first ripe, but the other basket had very bad figs, which could not be eaten, they were so bad. Then ADONAI said to me, "What do you see, Jeremiah?"

So I said, "Figs—the good figs are very good, but the bad are very bad, and cannot be eaten, they are so bad."

Then the word of ADONAI came to me, saying, thus says ADONAI, the God of Israel: "Like these good figs, so will I regard the exiles of Judah, whom I have sent out of this place to the land of the Chaldeans, as good. I will set My eyes on them as good. I will bring them back to this land, and I will build them up and not pull them down; I will plant them and not uproot them. Then I will give them a heart to know Me—for I am ADONAI—and they will be My people, and I will be their God. For they will return to Me with their whole heart."

Jeremiah 24:2-7

For thus says ADONAI: "After 70 years for Babylon are complete, I will visit you, and fulfill My good word toward you—to bring you back to this place. For I know the plans that I have in mind for you," declares ADONAI, "plans for *shalom* and not calamity—to give you a future and a hope.

Then you will call on Me, and come and pray to Me, and I will listen to you. You will seek Me and find Me, when you will search for Me with all your heart. Then I will be found by you," says ADONAI, "and I will return you from exile, and gather you from all the nations and from all the places where I have driven you," says ADONAI, "and I will bring you back to the place from which I removed you as captives into exile."

Jeremiah 29:10-14

The word came to Jeremiah from ADONAI, saying: thus says ADONAI, the God of Israel: "Write all the words that I have spoken to you in a scroll. For behold, the days are coming," declares ADONAI, "when I will return My people Israel and Judah from exile," declares ADONAI. "I will bring them back to the land that I gave to their fathers, and they will possess it."

Jeremiah 30:1-3

"Behold, days are coming"
—it is a declaration of ADONAI—
"when I will make a new covenant
with the house of Israel
and with the house of Judah—
not like the covenant
I made with their fathers
in the day I took them by the hand
to bring them out of the land of Egypt.
For they broke My covenant,
though I was a husband to them."
it is a declaration of ADONAI.
"But this is the covenant I will make with the
house of Israel after those days"
—it is a declaration of ADONAI—
"I will put My *Torah* within them.
Yes, I will write it on their heart.
I will be their God
and they will be My people.
No longer will each teach his neighbor
or each his brother, saying: 'Know ADONAI,'
for they will all know Me,
from the least of them to the greatest."
it is a declaration of ADONAI.
"For I will forgive their iniquity,
their sin I will remember no more."

Thus says ADONAI the Maker,
ADONAI who formed it to make it firm
—ADONAI is His Name.
"Call to Me, and I will answer you—
I will tell you great and hidden things,
which you do not know.

Jeremiah 33:2-3

"Behold, days are coming"
—it is a declaration of ADONAI—
"when I will fulfill the good word I spoke
concerning the house of Israel and concerning
the house of Judah.
In those days and at that time,
I will cause a Branch of Righteousness
to spring up for David,
and He will execute justice
and righteousness in the land.
In those days will Judah be saved,
and Jerusalem will dwell safely.
And this is the Name by which He will be called:
ADONAI our Righteousness."

Jeremiah 33:14-16

"In those days and at that time"
- it is a declaration of ADONAI-
"the children of Israel will come,
together with the children of Judah,
weeping as they come,
and will seek ADONAI their God.
They will ask about Zion, the way—
here are their faces! Come!
They will join themselves to ADONAI
in an everlasting covenant
that will never be forgotten."

Jeremiah 50:4-5

"Behold, days are coming"—it is a declaration of ADONAI—"when I will make a new covenant
with the house of Israel and with the house of Judah—
From Jeremiah 31:30 TLV ©2018, image #24/54

99

25. God Corrects Bad Behavior

Now the word of ADONAI came to Jonah, son of Amittai, saying: "Rise, go to the great city Nineveh and call out to her, for their evil has risen before me." But Jonah rose to flee to Tarshish, from the presence of ADONAI. He went down to Jaffa and found a ship going to Tarshish, paid the fee and went down into it to go with them to Tarshish—away from the presence of ADONAI.

Then ADONAI hurled a forceful wind into the sea and there was such a mighty storm on the sea that the ship was about to shatter. So the sailors were afraid and cried out, each man to his own god. Then they cast the cargo that was in the ship into the sea to lighten it. But Jonah had gone down into the lowest part of the ship, to lay down and fell fast asleep.

So the chief sailor came near to him and said to him, "What, are you sleeping? Get up! Call out to your god. Perhaps the gods will consider us, so we will not perish!"

Then each man said to his companion, "Come, let's cast lots—so we may know because of whom this evil is happening to us." So they cast lots and the lot fell on Jonah. Then they said to him, "Tell us, now! On whose account is this evil happening to us? What is your profession and where did you come from? What is your land and from what nation are you?"

He said to them, "I am a Hebrew, and I fear ADONAI God of the heavens, who made the sea and the dry land." Then the men became afraid with an overwhelming fear and they said to him, "What have you done?" For the men knew that he had fled from the presence of ADONAI, because he had told them.

So they said to him, "What should we do to you so the sea will become calm for us?"—for the storm was raging on.

"Pick me up and throw me into the sea," he said to them, "then the sea will become calm for you. For I know it is because of me that this great storm is upon you."

Nevertheless the men rowed hard to return to the land, but they could not, because the sea kept raging against them. So they cried to ADONAI and said, "Please, ADONAI, don't let us perish on account of the soul of this man and don't put innocent blood on us. For you, ADONAI, have done as you pleased." So they picked up Jonah and threw him into the sea—and the sea stilled from its raging. Then the men became afraid with an overwhelming fear of ADONAI, and they offered a sacrifice to ADONAI and made vows.

Jonah 1

Now ADONAI prepared a great fish to swallow Jonah, and Jonah was in the belly of the fish three days and three nights. Then Jonah prayed to ADONAI his God from the belly of the fish, saying: "From my distress I cried to ADONAI and He answered me. From the belly of Sheol I cried for help and you heard my voice. For you hurled me from the deep into the heart of the seas, and currents swirled around me. All your waves and your breakers swept over me."

And I said, "I have been banished from before your eyes. Yet I will continue to look toward your holy Temple. Waters surrounded me up to my soul. The deep sea engulfed me - reeds clung to my head. To the bottoms of the mountains I went down. The earth with her bars was around me, forever!

"Yet You brought my life up from the Pit, ADONAI my God. As my soul was fading from me, I remembered ADONAI and my prayer came to You, toward Your holy Temple. Those who watch worthless empty things forsake their mercy. But I, with a voice of thanks will sacrifice to you. What I vowed, I will pay. Salvation is from ADONAI ."

Then ADONAI spoke to the fish and it vomited Jonah onto the dry land.

Jonah 2

Now the word of ADONAI came to Jonah a second time, saying, "Rise and go to Nineveh, the great city, and cry out to it the proclamation that I am telling you." So Jonah rose and went to Nineveh according to the word of ADONAI.

Now Nineveh was a great city to God—the length of a three day journey. So Jonah began to come into the city for one day's journey, and he cried out saying: "Another forty days and Nineveh will be overthrown!"

Then the people of Nineveh believed God and called for a fast and wore sackcloth—from the greatest of them to the least of them. When the word reached the king of Nineveh, he rose from his throne, took off his robe, covered himself in sackcloth, and sat in the ashes.

He made a proclamation saying: "In Nineveh, by the decree of the king and his nobles, no man or beast, herd or flock, may taste anything. They must not graze nor drink water. But cover man and beast with sackcloth. Let them cry out to God with urgency. Let each one turn from his evil way and from the violence in his hands. Who knows? God may turn and relent, and turn back from his burning anger, so that we may not perish."

When God saw their deeds—that they turned from their wicked ways—God relented from the calamity that He said He would do to them, and did not do it.

Jonah 3

But it greatly displeased Jonah and he resented it. So he prayed to ADONAI and said, "Please, Lord, was not this what I said when I was still in my own country? That's what I anticipated, fleeing to Tarshish—for I knew that you are a gracious and compassionate God, slow to anger and full of kindness, and relenting over calamity. So please, ADONAI, take my soul from me—because better is my death than my life."

Yet ADONAI said, "Is it good for you to be so angry?"

So Jonah went out from the city and sat east of the city. There He made a sukkah and he sat under it, in the shade, until he saw what would happen in the city. Then ADONAI God prepared a plant and it grew up over Jonah, to give shade over his head to spare him from his discomfort. So Jonah was very happy about the plant. But God at dawn the next day prepared a worm that crippled the plant and it withered away.

When the sun rose, God prepared a scorching east wind, and the sun beat down on Jonah's head so that he became faint.

So he implored that his soul would die, saying, "My death would be better than my life!"

Then God said to Jonah, "Is it good for you to be so angry about the plant?"

"It is," he said, "I am angry enough to die!"

But ADONAI said, "You have pity on the plant for which you did no labor or make it grow, that appeared overnight and perished overnight. So shouldn't I have pity on Nineveh—the great city that has in it more than 120,000 people who don't know their right hand from their left—as well as many animals?"

Jonah 4

But I, with a voice of thanks will sacrifice to you. What I vowed, I will pay. Salvation is from ADONAI."
Then ADONAI spoke to the fish and it vomited Jonah onto the dry land.
From Jonah 2:10-11 TLV ©2018, image #25/54

26. God Tabernacles — With Us!

In the eighth month, in the second year of Darius, the word of ADONAI came to the prophet Zechariah, son of Berechiah son of Iddo, saying: "ADONAI has been furious with your fathers. Therefore tell them, thus says ADONAI-Tzva'ot, 'Return to Me' - it is a declaration of ADONAI-Tzva'ot - 'and I will return to you,' says ADONAI-Tzva'ot."

Zechariah 1:1-3

I lifted up my eyes – and behold, I saw a man with a measuring line in his hand. I asked, 'Where are you going?' He answered me, 'To measure Jerusalem to see how wide and how long it is.'

Zechariah 2:5-6

"'Sing and rejoice, O daughter of Zion! For behold, I am coming and I will live among you'— it is a declaration of ADONAI.

'In that day many nations will join themselves to ADONAI and they will be My people and I will dwell among you.'

Then you will know that ADONAI-Tzva'ot has sent me to you. ADONAI will inherit Judah as His portion in the holy land and will once again choose Jerusalem. Be silent before ADONAI, all flesh, for He has aroused Himself from His holy dwelling."

Zechariah 2:14-17

Then the angel who had been speaking with me returned and woke me—like a man who is wakened from his sleep. He asked me, 'What do you see?'
I replied, 'Behold, I see a solid gold menorah with its bowl at the top of it, and its seven lamps on it with seven pipes for the lamps that are on the top of it. Also two olive trees are by it, one on the right side of the bowl and the other on the left side of it.'
Then I responded by saying to the angel speaking with me, 'What are these, my lord?'

The angel who spoke with me responded by asking me, 'You do not know what these are?'
I replied, 'No, my lord.'

Then he responded to me by saying, 'This is the word of ADONAI to Zerubbabel saying: "Not by might, nor by power, but by My Ruach!" says ADONAI-Tzva'ot. "What are you, great mountain? Before Zerubbabel you will become a plain. He will bring out the capstone with shouts of "Grace, grace" to it.'"

Zechariah 4:1-7

Then the word of ADONAI-Tzva'ot came saying: "Thus says ADONAI-Tzva'ot, "I am exceedingly zealous for Zion, I am burning with jealousy for her."

Thus says ADONAI, "I will return to Zion and dwell in the midst of Jerusalem. Then Jerusalem will be called the City of Truth and the mountain of ADONAI-Tzva'ot will be called the Holy Mountain."

Thus says ADONAI-Tzva'ot, "Once again old men and old women will sit in the streets of Jerusalem, each with his staff in his hand because of his age. The streets of the city will be full of boys and girls playing in its streets."

"Thus says ADONAI-Tzva'ot, 'It may seem difficult in the eyes of the remnant of this people in those days, but will it also be difficult in My eyes?'—it is a declaration of ADONAI-Tzva'ot.

"Thus says ADONAI-Tzva'ot, 'Behold, I will save My people from the land of the east and from the land of the west. I will bring them back and they will live in the midst of Jerusalem. They will be My people and I will be their God, in truth and righteousness.'"

Zechariah 8:1-8

Rejoice greatly, daughter of *Zion*!

 Shout, daughter of Jerusalem!

Behold, your king is coming to you,

 a righteous one bringing salvation.

 He is lowly, riding on a donkey—

 on a colt, the foal of a donkey.

I will banish chariots from Ephraim

 and horses from Jerusalem,

 and the war bow will be broken.

He will speak *shalom* to the nations.

His rule will extend from sea to sea,

 from the River to the ends of the earth.

Zechariah 9:9-10

"Then I will pour out on the house of David and the inhabitants of Jerusalem a spirit of grace and supplication, when they will look toward Me whom they pierced. They will mourn for him as one mourns for an only son and grieve bitterly for him, as one grieves for a firstborn.

Zechariah 12:10

In that day His feet will stand on the Mount of Olives which lies to the east of Jerusalem, and the Mount of Olives will be split in two from east to west, forming a huge valley. Half of the mountain will move toward the north and half of it toward the south.

Then you will flee through My mountain valley because the mountain valley will reach to Azel. Yes, you will flee like you fled from the earthquake in the days of King Uzziah of Judah. Then *ADONAI* my God will come and all the *kedoshim* with Him.

In that day there will be no light, cold or frost. It will be a day known only to *ADONAI*, neither day nor night - even in the evening time there will be light.

Moreover, in that day living waters will flow from Jerusalem, half toward the eastern sea and half toward the western sea, both in the summer and in the winter.

ADONAI will then be King over all the earth. In that day *ADONAI* will be *Echad* and His Name *Echad*.

Zechariah 14:4-9

Then all the survivors from all the nations that attacked Jerusalem will go up from year to year to worship the King, *ADONAI-Tzva'ot*, and to celebrate *Sukkot*. Furthermore, if any of the nations on earth do not go up to Jerusalem to worship the King, *ADONAI-Tzva'ot*, they will have no rain.

Zechariah 14:16-17

This will be the punishment of Egypt and the punishment of all the nations that do not go up to celebrate *Sukkot*. In that day "Holy to *ADONAI*" will be inscribed on the bells of the horses and the pots in House of *ADONAI* will be like the sacred bowls in front of the altar.

In fact every pot in Jerusalem and in Judah will be Holy to *ADONAI-Tzva'ot*, so that everyone who comes to sacrifice will take them, and cook in them. In that day there will no longer be a Canaanite in the House of *ADONAI-Tzva'ot*.

Zechariah 14:19-21

Then all the survivors from all the nations that attacked Jerusalem will go up from year to year to worship the King, Adonai-Tzva'ot, and to celebrate Sukkot.

From Zechariah 14:16 TLV ©2018, image #26/54

27. God Is Our LORD

Psalm 1
Happy is the one who has not walked in the advice of the wicked,
nor stood in the way of sinners, nor sat in the seat of scoffers.
But his delight is in the *Torah* of ADONAI, and on His *Torah* he meditates day and night.
He will be like a planted tree over streams of water, producing its fruit during its season.
Its leaf never droops—but in all he does, he succeeds.
The wicked are not so.
For they are like chaff that the wind blows away.
Therefore the wicked will not stand during the judgment,
nor sinners in the congregation of the righteous.
For ADONAI knows the way of the righteous,
but the way of the wicked leads to ruin.

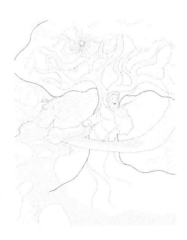

Psalm 19
The heavens declare the glory of God, and the sky shows His handiwork.
Day to day they speak, night to night they reveal knowledge.
There is no speech, no words, where their voice goes unheard.
Their voice has gone out to all the earth and their words to the end of the world.
In the heavens He pitched a tent for the sun.
It is like a bridegroom coming out of his bridal chamber.
It is like a strong man rejoicing to run his course.
It rises at one end of the heavens and makes its circuit to the other end.
Nothing is hidden from its heat.
The *Torah* of ADONAI is perfect, restoring the soul.
The testimony of ADONAI is trustworthy, making the simple wise.
The precepts of ADONAI are right, giving joy to the heart.

The *mitzvot* of A<small>DONAI</small> are pure, giving light to the eyes.

The fear of A<small>DONAI</small> is clean, enduring forever.

The judgments of A<small>DONAI</small> are true and altogether righteous.

They are more desirable than gold, yes, more than much pure gold!

They are sweeter than honey and drippings of the honeycomb.

Moreover by them Your servant is warned.

In keeping them there is great reward.

Who can discern his errors? Cleanse me of hidden faults.

Also keep Your servant from willful sins.

May they not have dominion over me.

Then I will be blameless, free from great transgression.

May the words of my mouth and the meditation of my heart

be acceptable before You, A<small>DONAI</small>, my Rock and my Redeemer.

Psalm 23

A<small>DONAI</small> is my shepherd, I shall not want.

He makes me lie down in green pastures.

He leads me beside still waters.

He restores my soul.

He guides me in paths of righteousness for His Name's sake.

Even though I walk through the valley of the shadow of death,

I will fear no evil, for You are with me:

Your rod and Your staff comfort me.

You prepare a table before me in the presence of my enemies.

You have anointed my head with oil, my cup overflows.

Surely goodness and mercy will follow me all the days of my life,

and I will dwell in the House of A<small>DONAI</small> forever.

But his delight is in the *Torah* of Adonai, and on His *Torah* he meditates day and night.
He will be like a planted tree over streams of water, producing its fruit during its season.
From Psalm 1:2-3 TLV ©2018, image #27/54

28. God Is Our Strength

Psalm 67

May God be gracious to us and bless us.

May He cause His face to shine upon us— *Selah*

So that Your way may be known on earth,

and Your salvation among all nations.

Let the peoples praise You, O God. Let all the peoples praise You.

Let the nations be glad and sing for joy, for You will judge the peoples fairly,

and guide the nations on the earth. *Selah*

Let the peoples praise You, O God. Let all the peoples praise You.

The earth has yielded its harvest— God, our God will bless us.

God will bless us, and all the ends of the earth will fear Him.

Psalm 84

How lovely are Your tabernacles, *ADONAI-Tzva'ot*!

My soul yearns, even faints, for the courts of *ADONAI*.

My heart and my flesh sing for joy to the living God.

Even the sparrow has found a home, and the swallow a nest for herself,

where she may lay her young—near Your altars, *ADONAI-Tzva'ot*— my King and my God!

Blessed are they who dwell in Your House —they are ever praising You. *Selah*

Blessed is one whose strength is in You, in whose heart are the pilgrim roads.

Passing through the valley of Baca, they make it a spring.

The early rain covers it with blessings.

They go from strength to strength—every one of them appears before God in Zion.

ADONAI-Tzva'ot, hear my prayer, give ear, O God of Jacob. *Selah*

O God, look at our shield, and look upon the face of Your anointed.

For a day in Your courts is better than a thousand anywhere else.

I would rather stand at the threshold of the House of my God

than dwell in the tents of wickedness.

For ADONAI Elohim is a sun and a shield.

ADONAI gives grace and glory.

No good thing will He withhold from those who walk uprightly.

ADONAI-Tzva'ot, blessed is the one who trusts in You.

Psalm 91

He who dwells in the shelter of Elyon, will abide in the shadow of Shaddai.

I will say of ADONAI, "He is my refuge and my fortress, my God, in whom I trust.

For He will rescue you from the hunter's trap and from the deadly pestilence.

He will cover you with His feathers, and under His wings you will find refuge.

His faithfulness is body armor and shield.

You will not fear the terror by night, nor the arrow that flies by day,

nor the plague that stalks in darkness, nor the scourge that lays waste at noon.

A thousand may fall at your side, and ten thousand at your right hand,

but it will not come near you.

You will only look on with your eyes and see the wicked paid back.

For you have made Elyon your dwelling, even ADONAI, who is my refuge,

so no evil will befall you nor any plague come near your tent.

For He will give His angels charge over you, to guard you in all your ways.

Upon their hands they will lift you up, lest you strike your foot against a stone.

You will tread upon the lion and cobra, trample the young lion and serpent.

"Because he has devoted his love to Me, I will deliver him.

I will set him securely on high, because he knows My Name.

When he calls on Me, I will answer him.

I will be with him in trouble, rescue him, and honor him.

With long life will I satisfy him and show him My salvation."

Even the sparrow has found a home, and the swallow a nest for herself, where she may lay her young
—near Your altars, ADONAI-*Tzva'ot*— my King and my God!

From *Psalm 84:4 TLV* ©2018, image #28/54

115

29. God Is Our Song

Psalm 100

A psalm of thanksgiving.

Shout joyfully to ADONAI, all the earth! Serve ADONAI with gladness.

Come before His presence with joyful singing. Know that ADONAI, He is God.

It is He who has made us, and we are His.

We are His people, the sheep of His pasture.

Enter His gates with thanksgiving and His courts with praise!

Praise Him, bless His Name. For ADONAI is good.

His lovingkindness endures forever, and His faithfulness to all generations.

Psalm 111

Halleluyah!

I praise ADONAI with all my heart in the company and congregation of the upright.

Great are the works of ADONAI—searched out by all who delight in them.

Glorious and majestic is His work, and His righteousness endures forever.

He made His wonders memorable.

ADONAI is gracious and full of compassion.

He gives food to those who fear Him.

He remembers His covenant forever.

He shows His people His powerful deeds, giving them the heritage of the nations.

The works of His hands are truth and justice.

All His precepts are trustworthy—they are upheld forever and ever, made in truth and uprightness.

He has sent redemption to His people.

He has ordained His covenant forever.

Holy and awesome is His Name.

The fear of ADONAI is the beginning of wisdom.

All who follow His precepts have good understanding.

His praise endures forever!

Psalm 133

Behold, how good and how pleasant it is for brothers to dwell together in unity!

It is like the precious oil upon the head,

coming down upon the beard—Aaron's beard—coming down on the collar of his robes.

It is like the dew of Hermon, coming down upon the mountains of Zion.

For there ADONAI commanded the blessing—life forevermore!

Psalm 150

Halleluyah!

Praise God in His Sanctuary!

Praise Him in His mighty expanse.

Praise Him for His acts of power.

Praise Him for His enormous greatness.

Praise Him with the blast of the *shofar.*

Praise Him with harp and lyre.

Praise Him with tambourine and dance.

Praise Him with string instruments and flute.

Praise Him with clash of cymbals.

Praise Him with resounding cymbals.

Let every thing that has breath praise ADONAI.

Halleluyah!

Praise Him with the blast of the *shofar*. Praise Him with harp and lyre.

Let every thing that has breath praise ADONAI. *Halleluyah!*

From Psalm 150:3-4,6 TLV ©2018, image #29/54

30. God Lets us Choose

Proverb 1
The fear of ADONAI is the beginning of knowledge,
but fools despise wisdom and discipline.
Hear, my son, your father's instruction
and forsake not your mother's teaching.
For they are a garland of grace for your head
and a chain to adorn your neck.
(verses 7-9)

Proverb 2
For ADONAI gives wisdom.
Out of His mouth comes knowledge and understanding.
He stores up sound wisdom for the upright.
He is a shield to those who walk in integrity.
He guards the paths of justice,
and protects the way of His kedoshim.
Then you will discern what is right
and just and fair—every good path.
For wisdom will enter your heart
and knowledge will be pleasant to your soul.
(verses 6-10)

Proverb 3
Let kindness and truth never leave you—
bind them around your neck,
write them on the tablet of your heart.
Then you will gain favor and a good name
in the eyes of God and man.
Trust in ADONAI with all your heart,
lean not on your own understanding.
In all your ways acknowledge Him,
and He will make your paths straight.
Do not be wise in your own eyes;
fear ADONAI and turn away from evil.
It will be healing to your body
and refreshment to your bones.
(verses 3-8)

Proverb 4

Listen, my son, and accept my words,
so the years of your life will be many.
I instructed you in the way of wisdom.
I have guided you along straight paths.
When you walk, your step will not be hindered,
and when you run, you will not stumble.
Hold on tightly to instruction, do not let it go—
guard it, for it is your life.
Do not enter the path of the wicked
or walk in the way of evil people.

(verses 10-14)

Proverb 5

For a man's ways are before the eyes of ADONAI,
and He observes all his paths.
The iniquities of a wicked man will ensnare him.
The cords of his sin will hold him down.
He will die for lack of discipline,
led astray by his own great folly.

(verses 21-23)

Proverb 6

Six things ADONAI hates,
yes, seven are abominations to Him:
haughty eyes,
a lying tongue,
hands that shed innocent blood,
a heart that plots wicked schemes,
feet that run to evil,
a false witness who spouts lies,
and one who stirs up strife among brothers.

(verses 16-19)

Proverb 7

My son, keep my words
and treasure my *mitzvot* within you.
Keep my *mitzvot* and live,
my teaching as the apple of your eye.
Bind them on your fingers,
write them on the tablet of your heart.

(verses 1-3)

He guards the paths of justice, and protects the way of His *kedoshim*.
Then you will discern what is right and just and fair—every good path.

From Proverbs 2:8-9 TLV ©2018, image #30/54

123

31. God Hears her Heart

It came to pass in the days when judges were governing, there was a famine in the land. A man went from the town of Bethlehem in Judah to dwell in the region of Moab with his wife and his two sons. The man's name was Elimelech, his wife's name was Naomi, and his two sons were named Mahlon and Chilion. They were Ephratites from Bethlehem in Judah. They came to the region of Moab and remained there.

Then Naomi's husband Elimelech died, so she was left with her two sons. They married Moabite women -one was named Orpah and the second was named Ruth, and they dwelt there about ten years. Then those two, Mahlon and Chilion, also died. So the woman was left without her children and her husband.

Then she got up, along with her daughters-in-law to return from the region of Moab, because in the region of Moab she had heard that ADONAI had taken note of His people and given them food. So she left the place where she was, along with her two daughters-in-law, and they started out on the road to return to the land of Judah.

So Naomi said to her two daughters-in-law, "Go, return each of you to your mother's house. May ADONAI show you the same kindness that you have shown to the dead and to me. May ADONAI grant that you find rest, each of you in the house of your own husband." Then she kissed them and they wept loudly.

"No!" they said to her, "we will return with you to your people." Now Naomi said, "Go back, my daughters! Why should you go with me? Do I have more sons in my womb who could become your husbands? ... '

Ruth 1:1-11

Again they broke into loud weeping. Then Orpah kissed her mother-in-law goodbye. But Ruth clung to her. She said, "Look, your sister-in-law is going back to her people and her gods. Return, along with your sister-in-law!"

Ruth replied, "Do not plead with me to abandon you, to turn back from following you. For where you go, I will go, and where you stay, I will stay. Your people will be my people, and your God my God. Where you die, I will die, and there I will be buried. May ADONAI deal with me, and worse, if anything but death comes between me and you!"

When she saw that Ruth was determined to go with her, she no longer spoke to Ruth about it.

Ruth 1:14-18

So Naomi and her daughter-in-law Ruth the Moabitess returned from the region of Moab. They arrived in Bethlehem at the beginning of the barley harvest.

Ruth 1:22

Now, Naomi had a relative on her husband's side—from Elimelech's family —a prominent man of substance whose name was Boaz.

Ruth the Moabitess, said to Naomi, "Please let me go out to the field and glean grain behind anyone in whose eyes I may find favor."

Naomi said to her, "Go ahead, my daughter."

So Ruth went out and gleaned in the field behind the reapers. She just so happened to be in the field of Boaz, who was from Elimelech's family.

Ruth 2:1-3

Her mother-in-law asked her, "Where did you glean today? Where did you work? May the one who noticed you be blessed!" She told her mother-in-law with whom she had worked and she said, "The name of the man for whom I worked is Boaz."

Ruth 2:19

Then Naomi said to her, "This man is closely related to us, one of our kinsmen-redeemers."

Then Ruth the Moabitess said, "He even said to me, 'Stay close to my workers until they have finished the entire harvest.'"

Naomi answered her daughter-in-law Ruth, "It is good, my daughter-in-law, that you go out with his female workers, so that you will not be harmed in another field." So she stayed close to Boaz's female workers, gleaning until both the barley harvest and the wheat harvest were completed. Meanwhile she lived with her mother-in-law.

Ruth 2:20b-23

Naomi her mother-in-law said to her "My daughter, should I not be seeking a resting place for you, so it may go well for you? Now, is Boaz, with whose female workers you have been, not our relative? Look, he will be winnowing barley tonight at the threshing floor. So bathe and perfume yourself, put on your cloak and go down to the threshing floor. But do not make yourself known to the man until he has finished eating and drinking. Let it be that when he lies down and you know the place where he lies down, go uncover his feet and lie down there. He will tell you what to do."

Ruth answered her, "I will do everything you say." So she went down to the threshing floor and did everything her mother-in-law had said.

Ruth 3:1-6

When Ruth came back to her mother-in-law, Naomi asked, "How did it go, my daughter?"

So Ruth told her all that the man had done for her. She said "He gave me six measures of barley, for he said, 'You shouldn't go back to your mother-in-law empty-handed.'"

"Wait, my daughter," Naomi said, "until you find out how the matter turns out, for he will not rest until he has settled the matter today."

Ruth 3:16-18

Meanwhile Boaz had gone up to the gate and sat down there. And all of a sudden, the *goel* about whom Boaz had spoken passed by.

"Come over," he called, "and sit down here, my friend." So he came over and sat down.

Then Boaz took ten of the town's elders and said, "Sit down here," so they sat down.

Ruth 4:1-2

Now in the past in Israel, one removed his sandal and gave it to another, in order to finalize the redemption and transfer of a matter. This was a legal transaction in Israel.

So the kinsman said to Boaz, "Buy it for yourself," then took off his shoe.

Boaz announced to the elders and all the people: "You are witnesses today that I have bought from Naomi all that belonged to Elimelech and all that belonged to Chilion and Mahlon. Moreover, I have acquired Ruth the Moabitess, the widow of Mahlon to be my wife in order to raise up the name of the deceased over his inheritance, so that the name of the deceased will not be cut off from his brothers or from the gate of his town. You are witnesses today."

Ruth 4:7-10

So Boaz took Ruth, and she became his wife. When he went to her, ADONAI enabled her to conceive, and she gave birth to a son.

Ruth 4:13

For where you go, I will go, and where you stay, I will stay. Your people will be my people, and your God my God.
From Ruth 1:16 TLV ©2018, image #31/54

32. God Appoints her Steps

This is what happened in the days of Ahasuerus, the Ahasuerus who reigned over 127 provinces from India to Ethiopia. At that time King Ahasuerus sat on his royal throne in the castle in Shushan. In the third year of his reign, he gave a banquet for all his princes and his servants. The military leaders of Persia and Media plus the nobles and officials of the provinces were present.

Esther 1:1-3

But Queen Vashti refused to come at the king's command conveyed by the eunuchs. Then the king became furious and burned with anger.

Esther 1:12

Then the king's servants who attended him said: "Let a search be made on the king's behalf for beautiful young virgins. … "

Esther 2:2

"… Then let the young woman who pleases the king become queen instead of Vashti." This advice pleased the king and he acted accordingly.

There was a Jewish man in the Shushan palace whose name was Mordecai, son of Jair son of Shimei, son of Kish, a Benjamite, who had been taken into exile from Jerusalem with the captives that had been carried away with King Jeconiah of Judah, whom King Nebuchadnezzar of Babylon had taken away.

He had raised Hadassah—that is Esther—his uncle's daughter, for she had neither father nor mother. The girl was attractive and had a beautiful figure. When her father and mother died, Mordecai took her to him as his own daughter.

After the king's order and decree became known, many young women were assembled in the palace of Shushan under the supervision of Hegai. Esther also was taken into the king's household under the supervision of Hegai, guardian of the women.

This young woman pleased him and found favor with him.

Esther 2:4-9a

Esther had not disclosed her people or her lineage, because Mordecai had commanded her not to make them known.

Esther 2:10

Now the king loved Esther more than all the other women, and she won his grace and favor more than all the other virgins. So he placed the royal crown upon her head and made her queen instead of Vashti.

Esther 2:17

Some time later King Ahasuerus promoted Haman, son of Hammedatha the Agagite, elevating him and setting his chair above all the officials who were with him.

All the king's servants who were at the king's gate bowed down and paid honor to Haman, for the king had commanded it. But Mordecai would not bow down or pay him honor.

Esther 3:1-2

When Haman saw that Mordecai was not bowing down or paying him honor, Haman was filled with rage.

Esther 3:5

Haman then said to King Ahasuerus: "There is a certain people scattered and dispersed among the peoples in all the provinces of your kingdom whose laws differ from those of every other people and who do not obey the king's laws.

It is not in the king's interest to tolerate them. If it pleases the king, let an edict be written to destroy them.

Esther 3:8-9a

The king's scribes were summoned in the first month, on the thirteenth day, and an edict was written as Haman had commanded.

Esther 3:12a

Dispatches were sent by couriers into all the king's provinces, stating to destroy, slay, and annihilate all the Jews—from the youth to the elderly, both little children and women—on a single day, the thirteenth day of the twelfth month, the month of Adar, and to plunder their possessions.

Esther 3:13

When Mordecai learned all that was done, he tore his clothes, put on sackcloth and ashes, and went out into the middle of the city crying out in a loud and bitter voice.

Esther 4:1

So Esther summoned Hathach, one of the king's eunuchs whom he had appointed to attend her, and ordered him to go to Mordecai to find the cause and reason for this.

Esther 4:5

He instructed her to go in to the king, to beg his favor and plead before him on behalf of her people.

Esther 4:8b

Mordecai told them to reply to Esther with this answer, "Do not think in your soul that you will escape in the king's household more than all the Jews. For if you remain silent at this time, relief and deliverance will arise for the Jews from another place—but you and your father's house will perish. Who knows whether you have attained royal status for such a time as this?"

Esther 4:13-14

Esther sent this reply to Mordecai, "Go! Gather together all the Jews who are in Shushan and fast for me. Do not eat or drink for three days, night or day. My maids and I will fast in the same way. Afterwards, I will go in to the king, even though it is not according to the law. So if I perish, I perish!" So Mordecai left and did all that Esther commanded him.

Esther 4:15-17

When the king saw Queen Esther standing in the courtyard, she found favor in his eyes, so the king held out to Esther the golden scepter in his hand and Esther approached and touched the top of the scepter.

Then said the king to her, "What is it, Queen Esther? Whatever you request, even as much as half of the kingdom, it will be given to you."

So Esther said, "If it pleases the king, let the king and Haman come this day to the banquet that I have prepared for him."

The king replied, "Bring Haman quickly so we may do what Esther said." Then the king and Haman came to the banquet that Esther prepared. As they were drinking wine, the king said to Esther, "What is your request? It will be granted to you. Whatever you request, even as much as half the kingdom, it will be fulfilled."

Esther 5:2-6

So the king and Haman came to dine with Queen Esther, and as they were drinking wine on the second day, the king asked Esther again, "Whatever you request, even as much as half of the kingdom, it will be given to you." So Queen Esther answered, "If I have found favor in the eyes of the king, and if it pleases the king, grant me my life—this is my petition. And spare the life of my people—this is my request!"

Esther 7:1-3

… So they hanged Haman on the gallows that he had prepared for Mordecai.

Esther 7:10a

The king granted the right for Jews in every city to assemble themselves and to protect themselves …

Esther 8:11

Mordecai recorded these events and he sent letters to all the Jews throughout the provinces of King Ahasuerus, both near and far, urging them to celebrate the fourteenth and fifteenth days of Adar every year as the days when the Jews got relief from their enemies, and as the month when their sorrow was turned into joy and their mourning into celebration. These were to be days of feasting, celebration and sending presents of food to one another and giving gifts to the poor.

Esther 9:20-22

For the Jews there was light and gladness, joy and honor. Throughout every province and throughout every city, wherever the king's edict and his law went, the Jews had gladness and joy, banquets and holidays.

From Esther 8:16-17 TLV ©2018, image #32/54

33. God Protects the Scribe

In the third year of the reign of King Jehoiakim of Judah, King Nebuchadnezzar of Babylon came to Jerusalem and besieged it. God gave King Jehoiakim of Judah into his hand, along with some of the vessels of the House of God. He brought them into the land of Shinar to the house of his god and put the vessels into the treasure house of his god.

Then the king told Ashpenaz the chief of his officials to bring in some of the sons of Israel from royal descent and nobility - youths without any defect, handsome, proficient in all wisdom, knowledgeable, intelligent and capable of serving in the king's palace.

Daniel 1:1-4a

Now among them were some from the sons of Judah: Daniel, Hananiah, Mishael and Azariah. The chief officer gave them new names: to Daniel, Belteshazzar; to Hananiah, Shadrach; to Mishael, Meshach; and to Azariah, Abed-nego.

Daniel 1:6-7

So Darius the Mede took over the kingdom at the age of 62. It pleased Darius to appoint 120 satraps to rule throughout the whole kingdom with three administrators over them, one of whom was Daniel.

These satraps were accountable to them so that the king would not be troubled. Now this Daniel was distinguishing himself among the supervisors and satraps because he had an extraordinary spirit in him. In fact, the king planned to appoint him over the entire kingdom.

At this time the supervisors and satraps tried to find ground for a charge against Daniel regarding the kingdom. But they were unable to find fault or corruption, because he was trustworthy and no negligence or dishonesty could be found in him.

Finally these men said, "We're not going to find any basis for charges against this man Daniel, unless we find something against him regarding the law of his God."

So these supervisors and satraps went in to the king as a group, and said to him, "King Darius, live forever! All the supervisors of the realm, the magistrates and satraps, ministers and governors, have all agreed that the king should issue an edict and enforce a decree that anyone who prays to any god or man for 30 days other than you O king, will be cast into the lions' den.

Now, O king, issue the decree and put it in writing so that it may not be altered, according to the law of the Medes and Persians, which cannot be repealed."

Thereupon King Darius issued the written decree.

Now when Daniel learned that a written decree had been issued, he went into his house, where the windows in his upper room opened toward Jerusalem. Three times a day he knelt down, prayed and gave thanks before his God, just as he did before. Then these men came as a group and found Daniel praying and making supplication before his God.

So they approached the king and spoke to him about the royal decree: "Didn't you issue a written decree that anyone who prays to any god or man for 30 days—except for you, O king—shall be cast into the den of lions?"

The king replied, "The decree stands, according to the law of the Medes and Persians, which cannot be repealed."

Daniel 6:1-13

Then they answered and said to the king: "Daniel, who is one of the exiles from Judah, pays no attention to you, O king, or to the decree that you put in writing. He still prays three times a day!"

When the king heard this report, he was deeply distressed, and he set his mind on how he might rescue Daniel. Until sunset he struggled to find a way to save him.

Then these men came as a throng in to the king, and said to the king: "Remember, O king, that it is a law of the Medes and Persians that no decree or edict which the king issues may be altered."

So the king gave the order and Daniel was brought and thrown into the lions' den. Now the king spoke to Daniel saying, "May your God, whom you serve continually, deliver you!"

A stone was brought to block the mouth of the den. The king sealed it with his own signet ring and with the signet of his nobles, so that nothing could be changed regarding Daniel. Then the king went to his palace and passed the night fasting - no entertainment was brought before him. He was unable to sleep.

At dawn the king got up and hurried to the lions' den. As he reached the den, he cried out to Daniel with a voice of anguish.

The king spoke out to Daniel saying: "Daniel, servant of the living God, was your God, whom you serve continually, able to rescue you from the lions?"

Daniel spoke to the king: "May the king live forever! My God sent His angel to shut the lions' mouths so that they haven't harmed me, because I was found innocent before Him. Nor have I committed any crime against you, O king."

Then the king was overjoyed, and ordered Daniel taken up out of the den. So Daniel was lifted out of the pit. No injury of any kind was found on him because he had trusted in his God.

Daniel 6:14-24

Then King Darius wrote to all the peoples, nations, and languages dwelling in all the earth: "May your peace be abundant! I issue a decree that in all the dominion of my kingdom people are to tremble with fear before the God of Daniel.

"For He is the living God, enduring forever!
His kingdom will never be destroyed,
His dominion will never end.
He delivers and rescues.
He performs signs and wonders
in the heavens and on earth.
He has delivered Daniel
from the power of the lions!"

So Daniel prospered during the reign of Darius and the reign of Cyrus the Persian.

Daniel 6:26-29

At dawn the king got up and hurried to the lions' den. As he reached the den, he cried out to Daniel with a voice of anguish. The king spoke out to Daniel saying: "Daniel, servant of the living God, was your God, whom you serve continually, able to rescue you from the lions?"

From Daniel 6:20-21 TLV ©2018, image #33/54

135

34. God Builds His House

The words of Nehemiah son of Hacaliah:

Now it happened that in the month of Kislev in the twentieth year, while I was in Shushan the capitol, that Hanani, one of my brothers, together with some men from Judah, arrived and I asked them about the Judeans, the remnant who had survived the captivity, and about Jerusalem.

They said to me, "The remnant who have survived the captivity there in the province are in great distress and disgrace. The wall of Jerusalem is broken down and its gates have been burned with fire."

Upon hearing these words I sat down and wept and mourned for days. I prayed and fasted before the God of heaven.

Then I said: "ADONAI, God of heaven, the great and awesome God who keeps the covenant and lovingkindness with those who love Him and keep His *mitzvot*, please let Your ear be attentive and Your eyes open to hear the prayer of Your servant that I am praying before You today both day and night on behalf of Your servants, *Bnei-Yisrael*.

I am confessing the sins of *Bnei-Yisrael* that we have sinned against You - yes, I and my ancestral house have sinned. We have acted very corruptly against You. We have not kept the *mitzvot*, the statutes, nor the rulings that You commanded Your servant Moses.

"Please recall the word that You commanded Your servant Moses, saying, 'If you act unfaithfully, I will scatter you among the peoples, but if you return to Me and obey My *mitzvot*, and do them, then even if your dispersed people are at the ends of the heavens, I will gather them from there, and bring them back to the place where I have chosen for My Name to dwell.'

"They are Your servants and Your people whom You redeemed by Your great strength and by Your mighty hand. Please, my Lord, let Your ear be attentive to the prayer of Your servant and to the prayer of Your servants who delight in revering Your Name. Give Your servant success today and grant compassion in the presence of this man." Now I was cupbearer to the king.

Nehemiah 1:1-11

Then in the month of Nisan, in the twentieth year of King Artaxerxes, when wine was set before him, I took the wine and gave it to the king. I had not been sad in his presence before.

So the king said to me, "Why is your face so sad when you are not ill? This can be nothing but sadness of heart."

I was very frightened, but I said to the king, "May the king live forever! Why should my face not be sad, when the city where my ancestors are buried lies in ruins and its gates have been destroyed by fire?"

The king asked me, "What is your request?"

Then I prayed to the God of heaven, and I answered the king, "If it seems good to the king and if your servant has found favor in your sight, send me to the city in Judah where my ancestors are buried that I may rebuild it."

Then the king, with the queen sitting beside him, asked me, "How long will your journey take, and when will you return?"

Since it pleased the king to send me, I set a time for him. I said to the king, "If it pleases the king, let him give me letters for the governors of Trans-Euphrates that will enable me to pass through until I arrive in Judah, as well as a letter to Asaph, the keeper of the king's forest so he will give me lumber to make beams for the gates of the fortress adjacent to the Temple, for the wall of the city and for the residence I will occupy."

The king granted me the requests because the good hand of my God was upon me.

Nehemiah 2:1-8

I came to Jerusalem, and after I was there for three days, I got up during the night along with a few men. But I did not tell anyone what my God had put in my heart to do for Jerusalem.

Nehemiah 2:11-12

The officials did not know where I had gone or what I was doing, but as yet I had not told the Jews, the *kohanim*, the nobles, the officials or the rest of the workers.

Then I said to them, "You see the bad situation we are in: Jerusalem is desolate and its gates have been burnt. Come! Let us rebuild the wall of Jerusalem so that we will no longer be a disgrace."Then I told them how the good hand of my God was on me and the words that the king had said to me. Then they replied, "Let us begin building!" So they prepared themselves for this good work.

Nehemiah 2:16-18

So we rebuilt the wall, and the entire wall was joined together up to half its height, for the people had a heart to work.

Nehemiah 3:38

Now when Sanballat, Tobiah, the Arabians, the Ammonites, and the people of Ashdod heard that restoration of the walls of Jerusalem was proceeding and that the breaches had begun to be closed, they became extremely angry. They all conspired together to come and fight against Jerusalem, and to stir up trouble against it. But we prayed to our God and stationed a guard against them day and night.

Nehemiah 4:1-3

From that day on, half of my men were doing the work, while half of them took hold of the spears, shields, bows and breastplates, and the leaders were behind the entire house of Judah. Those building the wall and those bearing heavy burdens kept one hand on the work and the other holding a weapon. So each of the builders had his sword strapped to his side while they were building, and the *shofar* blower was beside me.

Nehemiah 4:10-12

So the wall was completed on the twenty-fifth day of the month Elul, in just 52 days.

Nehemiah 6:15

Then the seventh month came and *Bnei-Yisrael* were in their towns.

Nehemiah 7:72b

Then all the people were brought as a single body into the plaza that was before the Water Gate. They said to Ezra the scribe, "Bring out the *Torah* scroll of Moses that ADONAI had commanded Israel."

Ezra the *kohen* brought the *Torah* before the assembly, which included men and women and all who could understand what they heard. This happened on the first day of the seventh month. So he read from it before the plaza in front of the Water Gate from first light until midday, in the presence of the men and women, and others who could understand. And all the people listened attentively to the scroll of the *Torah*.

Nehemiah 8:1-3

Now in the first year of King Cyrus of Persia—fulfilling the word of ADONAI by the mouth of Jeremiah—ADONAI stirred up the spirit of King Cyrus of Persia so that he sent a proclamation throughout all his kingdom and also put it in writing, saying: "Thus says King Cyrus of Persia 'ADONAI, the God of heaven, has given me all the kingdoms of the earth. He has appointed me to build Him a House in Jerusalem, which is in Judah. Whoever among you of all His people may go up and may ADONAI his God be with him.'"

2 Chronicles 36:22-23

So we rebuilt the wall, and the entire wall was joined together up to half its height, for the people had a heart to work.

From Nehemiah 3:38 TLV ©2018, image #34/54

35. God Hides The Savior

The book of the genealogy of *Yeshua ha-Mashiach, Ben-David, Ben-Avraham*: Abraham fathered Isaac, Isaac fathered Jacob, Jacob fathered Judah and his brothers, Judah fathered Perez and Zerah by Tamar, Perez fathered Hezron, Hezron fathered Ram, Ram fathered Amminadab, Amminadab fathered Nahshon, Nahshon fathered Salmon, Salmon fathered Boaz by Rahab, Boaz fathered Obed by Ruth, Obed fathered Jesse, and Jesse fathered David the king.

David fathered Solomon by the wife of Uriah, Solomon fathered Rehoboam, Rehoboam fathered Abijah, Abijah fathered Asa, Asa fathered Jehoshaphat, Jehoshaphat fathered Joram, Joram fathered Uzziah, Uzziah fathered Jotham, Jotham fathered Ahaz, Ahaz fathered Hezekiah, Hezekiah fathered Manasseh, Manasseh fathered Amon, Amon fathered Josiah, and Josiah fathered Jeconiah and his brothers at the time of the exile to Babylon.

After the Babylonian exile Jeconiah fathered Shealtiel, Shealtiel fathered Zerubbabel, Zerubbabel fathered Abiud, Abiud fathered Eliakim, Eliakim fathered Azor, Azor fathered Zadok, Zadok fathered Achim, Achim fathered Eliud, Eliud fathered Eleazar, Eleazar fathered Matthan, Matthan fathered Jacob, and Jacob fathered Joseph the husband of Miriam, from whom was born *Yeshua* who is called the Messiah.

So all the generations from Abraham to David are 14 generations, from David until the Babylonian exile are 14 generations, and from the Babylonian exile until the Messiah are 14 generations.

Matthew 1:1-17

And when they came into the house, they saw the Child with His mother Miriam; and they fell down and worshiped Him. Then, opening their treasures, they presented to Him gifts of gold, frankincense, and myrrh. And having been warned in a dream not to go back to Herod, they returned to their own country by another way.

Now when they had gone, behold, an angel of ADONAI appears to Joseph in a dream, saying, "Get up! Take the Child and His mother and flee to Egypt. Stay there until I tell you, for Herod is about to search for the Child, to kill Him."

So he got up, took the Child and His mother during the night, and went to Egypt. He stayed there until Herod's death. This was to fulfill what was spoken by ADONAI through the prophet, saying, "Out of Egypt I called My son."

Then when Herod saw that he had been tricked by the magi, he became furious. And he sent and killed all boys in Bethlehem and in all its surrounding area, from two years old and under, according to the time he had determined from the magi.

Matthew 2:11-16a

But when Herod died, behold, an angel of ADONAI appears in a dream to Joseph in Egypt, saying, "Get up! Take the Child and His mother and go to the land of Israel, for those seeking the Child's life are dead."

So he got up, took the Child and His mother, and went to the land of Israel. But hearing that Archelaus was king of Judea in place of his father Herod, he became afraid to go there. Then after being warned in a dream, he withdrew to the region of the Galilee. And he went and lived in a city called *Natzeret*, to fulfill what was spoken through the prophets, that *Yeshua* shall be called a *Natzrati*.

Matthew 2:19-23

When eight days had passed for His *brit-milah*, He was named *Yeshua*, the name given by the angel before He was conceived in the womb. And when the days of their purification were fulfilled, according to the *Torah* of Moses, they brought Him to Jerusalem to present to ADONAI.

As it is written in the *Torah* of ADONAI, "Every firstborn male that opens the womb shall be called holy to ADONAI."

So they offered a sacrifice according to what was said in the *Torah* of ADONAI: "a pair of turtle doves, or two young pigeons."

Now there was a man in Jerusalem whose name was Simeon, and this man was just and pious, waiting for the consolation of Israel. The *Ruach ha-Kodesh* was on him. And it had been revealed to him by the *Ruach ha-Kodesh* that he would not die before he had seen the Anointed One of ADONAI.

So in the *Ruach*, Simeon came into the Temple; and when the parents brought the Child *Yeshua* to do for Him according to the custom of the *Torah*, Simeon received Him into his arms and offered a *bracha* to God, saying,

"Now may You let Your servant go in peace,

O Sovereign Master,

according to Your word.

For my eyes have seen Your salvation,

which You have prepared

in the presence of all peoples:

'A light for revelation to the nations'

and the glory of Your people Israel."

And His father and mother were marveling at the things that were said about Him. And Simeon offered a *bracha* over them and said to Miriam His mother,

"Behold, this One is destined to cause the fall and rise of many in Israel, and to be a sign that is opposed, so the thoughts of many hearts may be uncovered. (And even for you, a sword will pierce through your soul.)"

Now Anna, a daughter of Phanuel of the tribe of Asher, was a prophetess. She was well advanced in age, having lived with a husband only seven years and then as a widow until age eighty-four.

She never left the Temple, serving night and day with fasting and prayers. And coming up at that very instant, she began praising God and speaking about the Child to all those waiting for the redemption of Jerusalem.

Luke 2:21-38

The Child kept growing and became strong, filled with wisdom; and the favor of God was upon Him.

Luke 2:40

For my eyes have seen Your salvation, which You have prepared in the presence of all peoples:
'A light for revelation to the nations' and the glory of Your people Israel."
From Luke 2:30, 32 TLV ©2018, image #35/54

36. God Speaks through His Son

"ADONAI your God will raise up for you a prophet like me from your midst—from your brothers. To him you must listen. This is just what you asked of ADONAI your God in Horeb on the day of the assembly when saying, 'I cannot continue to hear the voice of ADONAI my God or see this great fire any more, or I will die.'

"ADONAI said to me, 'They have done well in what they have spoken. I will raise up a prophet like you for them from among their brothers. I will put My words in his mouth, and he will speak to them all that I command him. Now whoever does not listen to My words that this prophet speaks in My Name, I Myself will call him to account.

Deuteronomy 18:15-19

The people walking in darkness
    will see a great light.
Upon those dwelling
in the land of the shadow of death,
    light will shine.
You will multiply the nation.
    You will increase the joy.
They will rejoice before You
    like the joy in the harvest,
as they revel when they divide spoil.

Isaiah 9:1-2a

For to us a child is born,
    a son will be given to us,
and the government will be upon His shoulder.
His Name will be called
    Wonderful Counselor,
    Mighty God
    My Father of Eternity,
    Prince of Peace.
Of the increase of His government
    and shalom there will be no end—

on the throne of David and over His kingdom—
    to establish it and uphold it
    through justice and righteousness
    from now until forevermore.
The zeal of ADONAI-Tzva'ot
    will accomplish this.

Isaiah 9:5-6

How can a young man keep his way pure?
By guarding it according to Your word.
With my whole heart have I sought You
—let me not stray from Your mitzvot.
 have treasured Your word in my heart,
so I might not sin against You.
Blessed are You, ADONAI.
Teach me Your statutes.
With my lips I rehearse
all the rulings of Your mouth.
I rejoice in the way of Your testimonies
above all wealth.
I will meditate on Your precepts,
and regard Your ways.
I will delight in Your decrees.
I will never forget Your word.

Psalm 119: 9-13

All of them are straightforward
to the discerning,
and right to those who find knowledge.
Receive my instruction instead of silver
and knowledge rather than choice gold.
For wisdom is better than jewels,
nothing you desire compares with her.
"I, wisdom, dwell with prudence,
and acquire knowledge with discretion.
To fear ADONAI is to hate evil.
I hate pride and arrogance,
evil behavior and a perverse mouth.
Counsel and sound wisdom are mine.
I have understanding and power.
By me kings reign
and princes decree justice.
By me princes govern,
and all nobles who judge righteously.
I love those who love me.
Those who earnestly seek me find me.
With me are wealth and honor,
enduring riches and righteousness.
My fruit is better than refined gold,
my harvest better than choice silver.
I walk in the way of righteousness,
along paths of justice.
I endow substance to those who love me
and fill their treasuries."

Proverbs 8:1-21

"So now, children, listen to me!
Blessed are those who keep my ways.
Heed discipline and be wise,
and do not neglect it.
Blessed is the one who listens to me,
watching daily at my gates,
waiting at my doorposts.

For whoever finds me finds life
and obtains favor from ADONAI.

Proverbs 8:32-35

Now His parents were going every year to Jerusalem for the Passover feast. When He became twelve years old, they were going up according to festival custom. As they headed home after completing the days, the boy *Yeshua* remained in Jerusalem; but His parents didn't know. Supposing He was in the caravan, they went a day's journey, then began looking for Him among relatives and friends. When they did not find Him, they returned to Jerusalem to search for Him.

After three days they found Him in the Temple, sitting in the center of the teachers, listening to them and asking them questions. And all those hearing Him were astonished at His understanding and His answers. When His parents saw *Yeshua*, they were overwhelmed. And His mother said to Him, "Child, why did you do this to us? Look, Your father and I were frantically searching for You!"

He said to them, "Why were you searching for Me? Didn't you know that I must be in My Father's house?" But they did not grasp the message He was telling them.

Then He went down with them to *Natzeret* and was obedient to them. But His mother treasured all these words in her heart. And *Yeshua* kept increasing in wisdom and stature, and in favor with God and men.

Luke 2:41-52

After three days they found Him in the Temple, sitting in the center of the teachers, listening to them and asking them questions. And all those hearing Him were astonished at His understanding and His answers. He said to them, "Why were you searching for Me? Didn't you know that I must be in My Father's house?"

From Luke 2:46-47 TLV ©2018, image #36/54

147

37. God Arrives!

There came a man sent from God, whose name was John. He came as a witness to testify about the light, so that through him everyone might believe. He was not the light, but he came to bear witness concerning the light. The true light, coming into the world, gives light to every man.

John 1:6-9

In those days, John the Immerser came proclaiming in the wilderness of Judea, "Turn away from your sins, for the kingdom of heaven is near!" For he is the one Isaiah the prophet spoke about, saying,

"The voice of one crying in the wilderness,

'Prepare the way of ADONAI, and make His paths straight.'"

Now John wore clothing from camel's hair and a leather belt around his waist, and his food was locusts and wild honey. Then Jerusalem was going out to him, and all Judea and all the region around the Jordan. Confessing their sins, they were being immersed by him in the Jordan River.

Matthew 3:1-6

"As for me, I immerse you in water for repentance. But the One coming after me is mightier than I am; I am not worthy to carry His sandals. He will immerse you in the *Ruach ha-Kodesh* and fire. His winnowing fork is in His hand, and He shall clear His threshing floor and gather His wheat into the barn; but the chaff He shall burn up with inextinguishable fire."

Then *Yeshua* came from the Galilee to John, to be immersed by him in the Jordan. But John tried to prevent Him, saying, "I need to be immersed by You, and You are coming to me?"

But *Yeshua* responded, "Let it happen now, for in this way it is fitting for us to fulfill all righteousness." So John yielded to Him.

After being immersed, *Yeshua* rose up out of the water; and behold, the heavens were opened to Him, and He saw the *Ruach Elohim* descending like a dove and coming upon Him.

And behold, a voice from the heavens said, "This is My Son, whom I love; with Him I am well pleased!"

Matthew 3:11-17

This is My Son, whom I love; with You I am well pleased

The next day, John sees *Yeshua* coming to him and says, "Behold, the Lamb of God who takes away the sin of the world! This is the One about whom I told you,

'He who comes after me is above me, because He was before me.'

I didn't know Him, but I came immersing with water so that He might be revealed to Israel."

Then John testified, "I have seen the *Ruach* coming down like a dove out of heaven, and it remained on Him. I did not know Him; but

149

the One who sent me to immerse in water said to me, 'The One on whom you see the *Ruach* coming down and remaining, this is the One who immerses in the *Ruach ha-Kodesh*.' And I have seen and testified that this is *Ben-Elohim*."

John 1:29-34

Then *Yeshua* was led by the *Ruach* into the wilderness to be tempted by the devil. After He had fasted for 40 days and 40 nights, He was hungry.

And when the tempter came to Him, he said, "If You are *Ben-Elohim*, tell these stones to become bread."

But He replied, "It is written, 'Man shall not live by bread alone, but by every word that comes from the mouth of God.'"

Then the devil took Him into the holy city and placed Him on the highest point of the Temple.

"If You are *Ben-Elohim*," he said, "throw Yourself down. For it is written,

"'He shall command His angels concerning you,'
and 'upon their hands they shall lift you up,
so that you may not strike your foot against a stone.'"

Yeshua said to him, "Again it is written, 'You shall not put ADONAI your God to the test.'"

Again, the devil takes Him to a very high mountain and shows Him all the kingdoms of the world and their glory.

And he said to Him, "All these things I will give You, if You fall down and worship me."

Then *Yeshua* says to him, "Go away, *satan*! For it is written,

'You shall worship ADONAI your God, and Him only shall you serve.'"

Then the devil leaves Him. And behold, angels came and began to take care of Him.

Now when *Yeshua* heard that John had been handed over, He withdrew to the Galilee. Leaving *Natzeret*, He came and settled in Capernaum, which is by the sea in the regions of Zebulun and Naphtali.

This was to fulfill what was spoken through Isaiah the prophet, saying,

"Land of Zebulun and land of Naphtali,
the way of the sea, beyond the Jordan,
Galilee of the nations—
the people sitting in darkness
have seen a great light,
and those sitting in the region
and shadow of death,
on them a light has dawned."

From then on, *Yeshua* began to proclaim, "Turn away from your sins, for the kingdom of heaven is near."

Matthew 4:1-17

This is My Son, whom I love; with You I am well pleased

And there came a voice from the heavens: "You are My Son, whom I love; with You I am well pleased!"

From Mark 1:11b TLV ©2018, image #37/54

38. God Feeds the Hungry

Yeshua returned in the power of the *Ruach* to the Galilee, and news about Him went out through all the surrounding region. He taught in their synagogues, and everyone was praising Him. And He came to *Natzeret*, where He had been raised. As was His custom, He went into the synagogue on *Shabbat*, and He got up to read. When the scroll of the prophet Isaiah was handed to Him, He unrolled the scroll and found the place where it was written,

"The *Ruach ADONAI* is on me,

because He has anointed me

to proclaim Good News to the poor.

He has sent me to proclaim release to the captives

and recovery of sight to the blind,

to set free the oppressed,

and to proclaim the year of *ADONAI's* favor."

He closed the scroll, gave it back to the attendant, and sat down. All eyes in the synagogue were focused on Him. Then He began to tell them, "Today this Scripture has been fulfilled in your ears."

Luke 4:14-21

Yeshua came down to Capernaum, a town in the Galilee. He was teaching them on *Shabbat*, and they were astounded at His teaching because His message had authority.

Luke 4:31-32

It happened that the crowds were pressing upon *Yeshua* to hear the word of God as He was standing by the Lake of *Kinneret*, when He saw two boats standing beside the lake. Now the fishermen had left them and were washing the nets. Getting into one of the boats, Simon's boat, *Yeshua* asked him to push out a ways from the land. Then sitting down, He taught the crowds from the boat.

When He had finished speaking, He said to Simon, "Go out into the deep water and let down your nets for a catch."

Simon replied, "Master, we've worked hard all night and caught nothing. But at Your word I will let down the nets." When they had done this, they caught so many fish that their nets began to break. So they signaled to their partners in the other boat to come and help them. They came and filled both boats so full that they began to sink.

But when Simon Peter saw this, he fell down at *Yeshua's* knees, saying, "Go away from me, Master, for I am a sinful man!" For amazement had gripped him and all who were with him, over the catch of fish they had netted; so also Jacob and John, Zebedee's sons, who were partners with Simon.

But *Yeshua* said to Simon, "Do not be afraid. From now on, you will be catching men." So when they had brought the boats to the landing, they left everything and followed Him.

Now while *Yeshua* was in one of the towns, a man covered with *tzara'at* appeared. And when he saw *Yeshua*, he fell on his face and begged Him, saying, "Master, if You are willing, You can make me clean."

Yeshua stretched out His hand and touched him, saying, "I am willing. Be cleansed!" Immediately, the *tzara'at* left him. *Yeshua* ordered him to tell no one, but commanded him, "Go and show yourself to the *kohen*. Then bring an offering for your cleansing, just as Moses commanded, as a testimony to them."

But the news about *Yeshua* was spreading all the more, and many crowds were coming together to hear and to be healed of their diseases. Yet He would often slip away into the wilderness and pray.

Luke 5:1-16

And it was during these days that *Yeshua* went out to the mountain to pray, and He spent all night in prayer to God. When day came, He called His disciples, choosing from among them twelve whom He also named emissaries—

Simon, whom He also named Peter, and Andrew his brother; and Jacob and John; and Philip and Bartholomew; and Matthew and Thomas; Jacob the son of Alphaeus; Simon who was called the Zealot; Judah the son of Jacob; and Judah from Kriot, who became a traitor.

Then *Yeshua* came down with them and stood on a level place. A large crowd of His disciples and a multitude of people, from all Judea, Jerusalem, and the coastal region of Tyre and Sidon, had come to hear Him and to be healed of their diseases. Even those disturbed by defiling spirits were being healed. Everyone in the crowd was trying to touch Him, because power flowed from Him and He was healing them all.

And looking up at His disciples, He said,

"Blessed are you who are poor,

for yours is the kingdom of God.

Blessed are you who hunger now,

for you shall be satisfied.

Blessed are you who weep now,

for you shall laugh.

Blessed are you when people hate you,

and when they exclude you,

and revile you,

and spurn your name as evil

on account of the Son of Man.

"Rejoice in that day and jump for joy! For behold, your reward is great in heaven! For their fathers used to treat the prophets the same way.

Luke 6:12-23

"But I say to you who are listening: Love your enemies, do good to those who hate you, bless those who curse you, pray for the ones who mistreat you. To the one who strikes you on the cheek, offer the other also. And from the one who takes your cloak, do not hold back your shirt. Give to every one who asks you; and whoever takes something of yours, make no demands upon him.

"Do to others as you would have them do to you. If you love those who love you, what credit is that to you? For even sinners love those who love them. And if you do good to those who are doing good to you, what credit is that to you? Even sinners do this. And if you lend to those from whom you expect to take, what credit is that to you? Even sinners lend to sinners in order to receive back the same.

"But love your enemies, and do good, and lend, expecting nothing in return. Then your reward will be great and you will be sons of *Elyon*, for He is kind to the ungrateful and evil ones. Be compassionate, just as your Father is compassionate to you.

"Do not judge, and you will not be judged. Do not condemn, and you will not be condemned. Pardon, and you will be pardoned. Give, and it will be given to you—a good measure, pressed down, shaken together, overflowing, will be given into your lap. For whatever measure you measure out will be measured back to you."

Luke 6:27-38

When He had finished speaking, He said to Simon, "Go out into the deep water and let down your nets for a catch."

From Luke 5:4b TLV ©2018, image #38/54

39. God Invites Little Children

Come, children, listen to me:
I will teach you the fear of ADONAI.
Who is the one who delights in life,
and loves to see good days?
Keep your tongue from evil,
and your lips from speaking treachery.
Depart from evil and do good.
Seek *shalom* and pursue it.

Psalm 34:12-15

A contemplative song of Asaph.
 Listen, my people, to my teaching.
 Turn your ears to the words of my mouth.
 I will open my mouth with a parable.
 I will utter perplexing sayings from of old,
 which we have heard and known,
     and our fathers have told us.
We will not hide them from their children,
telling to the next generation
the praises of ADONAI
     and His strength and the wonders
     He has done.
For He established a testimony in Jacob
and ordained *Torah* in Israel,
which He commanded our fathers
to teach their children,
so that the next generation might know,
     even the children yet to be born:
     they will arise and tell their children.
Then they will put their trust in God,
not forgetting the works of God,
but keeping His *mitzvot*.

Psalm 78:1b-7

Then they came to Capernaum. And when *Yeshua* was in the house, He began to ask the disciples, "What were you discussing on the way?"

But they kept quiet, because on the way they had argued with one another about who was the greatest.

Sitting down, He called the Twelve and said to them, "If any man wants to be first, he shall be least of all and the servant of everyone."

Taking a small child, He set him in the midst of them. And taking him in His arms, He said to them, "Whoever welcomes one of these children in My name, welcomes Me; and whoever welcomes Me, welcomes not Me but the One who sent Me."

John said to Him, "Teacher, we saw someone driving out demons in Your name, and we tried to stop him because he wasn't following us."

But *Yeshua* responded, "Don't stop him! No one who does a miracle in My name will be able soon afterward to speak evil about Me. He who is not against us is for us. For whoever gives you a cup of water to drink in My name because you belong to Messiah, amen I tell you, he will never lose his reward."

"But whoever causes one of these little ones who trust in Me to stumble, it would be better for him to have a heavy millstone put around his neck and to be thrown into the sea!"

Mark 9:33-42

"See that you do not despise one of these little ones, for I tell you that their angels in heaven continually see the face of My Father in heaven.

"What do you think? If a certain man has 100 sheep and one of them goes astray, won't he leave the 99 on the mountains and go looking for the one that is straying? And if he finds it, amen I tell you, he rejoices over it more than over the 99 that didn't stray. Even so, it's not the will of your Father in heaven that one of these little ones should be lost."

Matthew 18:10-14

Now people were bringing little children to *Yeshua* so He might touch them, but the disciples rebuked those who brought them. But when *Yeshua* saw this, He got angry.

He told them, "Let the little children come to Me! Do not hinder them, for the kingdom of God belongs to such as these. Amen, I tell you, whoever does not receive the kingdom of God like a little child will never enter it!"

And He took them in His arms and began blessing them, laying His hands on them.

Mark 19:13-16

Then little children were brought to *Yeshua* so that He might lay hands upon them and pray. Then the disciples rebuked those who brought them.

But *Yeshua* said, "Let the little children come to Me and do not hinder them, for the kingdom of heaven belongs to such as these." After laying His hands upon them, He went on from there.

Now behold, one came to Him and said, "Teacher, what good shall I do to have eternal life?

"Why do you ask Me about what is good?" *Yeshua* said to him. "There is only One who is good; but if you want to enter into life, keep the commandments."

"Which ones?" he said.

Yeshua said, "'Do not murder, do not commit adultery, do not steal, do not give false testimony, honor your father and mother,' and 'love your neighbor as yourself.'"

"All these I've kept," the young man said to Him. "What do I still lack?"

Yeshua said to him, "If you wish to be perfect, go, sell what you own, and give to the poor; and you will have treasure in heaven. Then come, follow Me."

But when the young man heard this statement, he went away grieving, for he had much property.

Then *Yeshua* said to His disciples, "Amen, I tell you, it is hard for a rich man to enter the kingdom of heaven. Again I tell you, it is easier for a camel to go through the eye of a needle, than for a rich man to enter the kingdom of God."

When the disciples heard this, they were utterly astonished and said, "Then who can be saved?"

And looking, *Yeshua* said to them, "With men this is impossible, but with God all things are possible."

Matthew 19:13-26

But *Yeshua* said, "Let the little children come to Me and do not hinder them,
for the kingdom of heaven belongs to such as these."

From Matthew 19:14 TLV ©2018, image #39/54

40. God is Our Father

"When you pray, do not be like the hypocrites; for they love to pray standing in the synagogues and on the street corners, so that they may be seen by others. Amen, I tell you, they have their reward in full!

"But you, when you pray, go into your inner room; and when you have shut your door, pray to your Father who is in secret. And your Father, who sees in secret, shall reward you. And when you are praying, do not babble on and on like the pagans; for they think they will be heard because of their many words. Do not be like them, for your Father knows what you need before you ask Him.

"Therefore, pray in this way:

"'Our Father in heaven,

sanctified be Your name.

Your kingdom come,

Your will be done

on earth as it is in heaven.

Give us this day our daily bread.

And forgive us our debts

as we also have forgiven our debtors.

And lead us not into temptation,

but deliver us from the evil one.'

"For if you forgive others their transgressions, your heavenly Father will also forgive you. But if you do not forgive others, neither will your Father forgive your transgressions.

Matthew 6:5-15

The twelve emissaries gathered together with *Yeshua*, and they reported to Him all they had done and taught. There were many coming and going, and they had no time even to eat.

So He said to them, "Come away by yourselves to an isolated place and rest awhile."

So they left privately by boat to an isolated place. However, the people saw them leaving, and many recognized them.

They ran on foot from all the towns to get there ahead of them. As *Yeshua* came ashore, He saw a large crowd and felt compassion for them, because they were like sheep without a shepherd. So He taught them many things.

When it was already late, His disciples came to Him and said, "This place is isolated, and the hour is already late. Send these people away so they can go into the nearby countryside and the villages and buy themselves something to eat."

But He answered and said to them, "You give them something to eat!"

And they said to Him, "Should we go and spend 200 denarii on bread to give them something to eat?"

Then He said to them, "How many loaves do you have? Go and see."

When they found out, they said, "Five, and two fish."

Then *Yeshua* made them all sit down in groups on the green grass. So they reclined in groups of hundreds and fifties. And He took the five loaves and the two fish; and looking up to heaven, He offered the *bracha*.

He broke the loaves and kept giving them to the disciples to serve to the people; and He divided the two fish among them all. They all ate and were satisfied, and the disciples picked up twelve baskets full of broken pieces and fish.

Now there were 5,000 men who ate the loaves.

Mark 6:30-44

"So I say to you, do not worry about your life—what you will eat or drink, or about your body, what you will wear. Isn't life more than food and the body more than clothing?

"Look at the birds of the air. They do not sow or reap or gather into barns; yet your Father in heaven feeds them. Are you not of more value than they? And which of you by worrying can add a single hour to his life? And why do you worry about clothing? Consider the lilies of the field, how they grow. They neither toil nor spin.

"Yet I tell you that not even Solomon in all his glory clothed himself like one of these. Now if in this way God clothes the grass—which is here today and thrown into the furnace tomorrow—will He not much more clothe you, O you of little faith?

"Therefore, do not worry, saying,

'What will we eat?' or 'What will we drink?' or 'What will we wear?' For the pagans eagerly pursue all these things; yet your Father in heaven knows that you need all these. But seek first the kingdom of God and His righteousness, and all these things shall be added to you.

"Therefore do not worry about tomorrow, for tomorrow will worry about itself. Each day has enough trouble of its own."

Matthew 6:25-34

"Ask, and it shall be given to you. Seek, and you shall find. Knock, and it shall be opened to you. For everyone who asks receives, and the one who seeks finds, and to the one who knocks it shall be opened.

"For what man among you, when his son asks him for bread, will give him a stone? Or when he asks for a fish, will give him a snake? If you then, being evil, know how to give good gifts to your children, how much more will your Father in heaven give good things to those who ask Him!

Matthew 7:7-11

In those days, there was another large crowd with nothing to eat, and *Yeshua* called the disciples.

He said to them, "I have compassion for the crowd, because they've stayed with Me for three days now and have nothing to eat. If I send them home hungry they'll pass out on the way, for some of them have come from very far away."

His disciples answered Him, "How can anyone satisfy these people with bread here in a wasteland?"

"How many loaves do you have?" *Yeshua* was asking them.

"Seven," they said.

He directed the crowd to recline on the ground. After taking the seven loaves and giving thanks, He broke them and began giving them to His disciples to serve; and they served them to the crowd. They also had a few small fish and, after offering a *bracha* for them, He commanded these to be served as well. They ate and were satisfied, and they picked up the broken pieces left over—seven baskets. About four thousand were there, and *Yeshua* sent them away.

Mark 8:1-9

When they came to Capernaum, the collectors of the Temple tax came to Peter and said, "Your teacher pays the Temple tax, doesn't He?"

"Yes," Peter said.

Now when Peter came into the house, *Yeshua* spoke to him first, saying, "What do you think, Simon? The kings of the earth, from whom do they collect tolls or tax? From their sons or from strangers?"

After Peter said, "From strangers,"

Yeshua said to him, "Then the sons are free. But so that we do not offend them, go to the sea and throw out a hook, and take the first fish that comes up. And when you open its mouth, you'll find a coin. Take that, and give it to them, for Me and you."

Matthew 17:24-27

And He took the five loaves and the two fish; and looking up to heaven, He offered the *bracha*. He broke the loaves and kept giving them to the disciples to serve to the people; and He divided the two fish among them all.

From Mark 6:41 TLV ©2018, image #40/54

41. God Blesses *Yeshua*

Baruch ha-Ba b'Shem ADONAI—
Blessed is He who comes
in the Name of ADONAI.
We bless you from the House of ADONAI.
ADONAI is God, and He has given us light.
Join the festival with branches,
up to the horns of the altar.
You are my God, and I praise You.
You are my God—I exalt You!
Praise ADONAI, for He is good,
for His lovingkindness endures forever.

Psalm 118:26-29

The next day, the huge crowd that had come up for the feast heard that *Yeshua* was coming to Jerusalem.

John 12:12

Now as they draw near to Jerusalem, to Bethphage and Bethany, to the Mount of Olives, *Yeshua* sends two of His disciples and says to them, "Go into the village ahead of you. Right away as you enter it, you will find a colt tied up that no one has ever sat upon. Untie it and bring it. If anyone says to you, 'Why are you doing this?' say, 'The Master needs it.' And right away he will send it back here."

They went and found a colt outside in the street, tied at a door. And they untied it. Some people standing there began saying to them, "What are you doing, untying the colt?"

They answered just as *Yeshua* had told them, and the people let them go.

Mark 11:1-6

This happened to fulfill what was spoken through the prophet, saying,

"Say to the daughter of Zion,
'See, your King is coming to you,
humble and sitting on a donkey,
a colt, the foal of a donkey.'"

The disciples went and did as *Yeshua* had directed them. They brought the donkey and colt and put their clothing on them, and He sat on the clothing. Most of the crowd spread their clothing on the road, and others began cutting branches from the trees and spreading them on the road.

The crowds going before Him and those following kept shouting, saying,

"*Hoshia-na* to *Ben-David*!
Baruch ha-Ba b'Shem ADONAI!
Blessed is He who comes
in the name of the LORD!
Hoshia-na in the highest!"

When He entered Jerusalem, the whole city was stirred up, saying, "Who is this?"

And the crowds kept saying, "This is the prophet *Yeshua*, from *Natzeret* in the Galilee."

Then *Yeshua* entered the Temple and drove out all those selling and buying in the Temple. He overturned the tables of the moneychangers and the seats of those selling doves.

And He said to them, "It is written, 'My house shall be called a house of prayer,' but you are making it 'a den of thieves'!"

The blind and lame came to Him in the Temple, and He healed them. But when the ruling *kohanim* and *Torah* scholars saw the wonders He performed, and the children crying out in the Temple and saying, "*Hoshia-na* to *Ben-David*," they became indignant.

And they said to Him, "Do You hear what these children are saying?"

"Yes," *Yeshua* said to them. "Haven't you ever read,

"'Out of the mouth of babes and nursing toddlers

You have prepared praise for Yourself '?"

Then He left them and went out of the city to Bethany, and He spent the night there.

Matthew 21:4-17

Now early in the morning, as He was returning to the city, He became hungry. Seeing a lone fig tree by the road, He came up to it and found nothing on it except leaves only.

And He said to it, "May no fruit ever come from you again!" And the fig tree shriveled up at once.

When the disciples saw it they were astonished. "How did the fig tree shrivel on the spot?" they asked.

Yeshua answered them, "Amen, I tell you, if you have faith and do not doubt, not only will you do what was done to the fig tree, but even if you say to this mountain, 'Be taken up and thrown into the sea,' it will happen. And whatever you ask in prayer, trusting, you shall receive."

Now when He entered the Temple, the ruling *kohanim* and the elders of the people came to Him while He was teaching, saying, "By what authority are You doing these things? Who gave You this authority?"

Yeshua replied to them, "I also will ask you one question. If you tell Me, I likewise will tell you by what authority I do these things. John's immersion, where was it from? From heaven or from men?"

They began to dialogue among themselves, saying, "If we say, 'From heaven,' He will say to us,

'Then why didn't you believe him?'

But if we say, 'From men,' we fear the crowd, for all hold up John as a prophet."

So answering *Yeshua*, they said, "We don't know."

Then He said to them, "Neither am I telling you by what authority I do these things."

Matthew 21:18-27

In that hour, some Pharisees came up and said to *Yeshua*, "Get out and leave from here, because Herod wants to kill You!"

But *Yeshua* said to them, "Go and tell that fox,

'Indeed, I'm driving out demons and performing healings today and tomorrow, and on the third day I will reach My goal.'

But I must keep going today and tomorrow because it just can't be that a prophet would perish outside Jerusalem.

"O Jerusalem, Jerusalem who kills the prophets and stones those sent to her! How often I longed to gather your children together, as a hen gathers her chicks under her wings, but you were not willing. Look, your house is left to you desolate!

"For I tell you, you will never see Me until you say, '*Baruch ha-Ba b'Shem* ADONAI. Blessed is He who comes in the name of the LORD!'"

Luke 13:31-35

"Hoshia-na to Ben-David! Baruch ha-Ba b'Shem Adonai!
Blessed is He who comes in the name of the Lord! *Hoshia-na* in the highest!"
From Matthew 21:9 TLV ©2018, image #41/54

42. God Remembers the Passover

Now it happened that when *Yeshua* had finished all these words, He said to His disciples, "You know that Passover comes in two days, and the Son of Man will be handed over to be executed."

Then the ruling *kohanim* and elders of the people were gathered together in the court of the *kohen gadol* named Caiaphas. They plotted together in order that they might seize *Yeshua* by stealth and kill Him. "But not during the festival," they were saying, "so there won't be a riot among the people."

Now while *Yeshua* was in Bethany at the house of Simon *ha-Metzora*, a woman came up to Him with an alabaster jar of very expensive oil. And she poured it on His head as He was reclining at the table. But when the disciples saw this, they were indignant, saying, "Why this waste? It could have been sold for a lot, and the money given to the poor!"

But *Yeshua*, knowing this, said to them, "Why do you cause trouble for this woman? She's done Me a *mitzvah*. You always have the poor with you, but you won't always have Me. For when she poured this oil on My body, she did it to prepare Me for burial. Amen, I tell you, wherever this Good News is proclaimed in all the world, what she has done will also be told in memory of her."

Then one of the Twelve, the one called Judah of Kriot, went to the ruling *kohanim* and said, "What are you willing to give me if I hand Him over to you?" And they weighed out thirty shekels of silver for him. From then on, Judah began looking for a chance to hand Him over.

Matthew 26:1-16

Then came the day of *matzah* when the Passover lamb had to be sacrificed. Now *Yeshua* sent Peter and John, saying, "Go and prepare the Passover for us, so we may eat."

Then they said to Him, "Where do You want us to prepare?"

And He said to them, "Behold, when you have entered the city, a man carrying a jar of water will meet you. Follow him into the house that he enters. And say to the owner of the house, 'The Teacher says to you, "Where is the guest room where I may eat the Passover with My disciples?"' And with that, he will show you a large upper room, fully furnished. Make preparations there." So they left and found just what *Yeshua* had told them, and they prepared the Passover.

Luke 22:7-13

While the *seder* meal was happening, the devil had already put in the heart of Judah from Kriot that he should hand over *Yeshua*. *Yeshua* knew that the Father had given all things into His hands, and that He had come from God and was returning to God. So He gets up from the meal and lays aside His outer garment; and taking a towel, He wrapped it around His waist. Then He pours water into a basin. He began to wash the disciples' feet, drying them with the towel wrapped around Him.

Then He comes to Simon Peter, who says to Him, "Master, are You going to wash my feet?"

Yeshua responded, "You don't know what I am doing now, but you will understand after these things."

Peter said to Him, "You shall never wash my feet!"

Yeshua answered him, "If I don't wash you, you have no part with Me."

Simon Peter said to Him, "Master, then not only my feet, but also my hands and my head!"

Yeshua said to him, "He who has bathed has no need to wash, except the feet; he is completely clean. And you all are clean, though not every one." He knew who was betraying Him; for this reason, He said, "Not all of you are clean."

So after He had washed their feet and put His robe back on and reclined again, He said to them, "Do you understand what I have done for you? You call Me 'Teacher' and 'Master'—and rightly you say, for I am. So if I, your Master and Teacher, have washed your feet, you also ought to wash each other's feet. I have given you an example—you should do for each other what I have done for you.

"Amen, amen I tell you, a servant isn't greater than his master, and the one who is sent isn't greater than the one who sent him. If you know these things, you are blessed if you do them!"

John 13:10-17

Now while they were eating, *Yeshua* took *matzah*; and after He offered the *bracha*, He broke and gave to the disciples and said, "Take, eat; this is My body."

And He took a cup; and after giving thanks, He gave to them, saying, "Drink from it, all of you; for this is My blood of the covenant, which is poured out for many for the removal of sins. But I say to you, I will never drink of this fruit of the vine from now on, until that day when I drink it anew with you in My Father's kingdom."

Matthew 26:26-29

After He said these things, *Yeshua* was agitated in spirit and testified, "Amen, amen I tell you, one of you will betray Me!"

The disciples began looking at each other, perplexed—who was He talking about? One of His disciples, whom *Yeshua* loved, was reclining at His side.

Simon Peter nods to him and says, "Ask Him—who is He talking about?"

Then he who leaned on *Yeshua's* chest says to Him, "Master, who is it?"

Yeshua answers, "It's the one I will give this bit of *matzah* to, after I dip it."

After dipping the *matzah*, He takes it and gives it to Judah from Kriot, the son of Simon. And with that bit, *satan* entered into him.

Then *Yeshua* tells him, "What you're about to do, do quickly!"

John 13:21-27

Then when Judah had gone out, *Yeshua* said, "Now the Son of Man is glorified, and God is glorified in Him! If God is glorified in Him, God will glorify Him in Himself, and will glorify Him at once. Little children, I am with you only a little longer. You will search for Me; and just as I told the Judean leaders, so I say to you now, 'Where I am going, you cannot come.'

"I give you a new commandment, that you love one another. Just as I have loved you, so also you must love one another. By this all will know that you are My disciples, if you have love for one another."

John 13:31-35

After singing the *Hallel*, they went out to the Mount of Olives.

Matthew 26:30

Now while they were eating, *Yeshua* took *matzah*; and after He offered the *bracha*,
He broke and gave to the disciples and said, "Take, eat; this is My body."
From Matthew 26:26 TLV ©2018, image #42/54

171

43. God Chooses the Scapegoat

And *Yeshua* said to them, "You will all fall away, for it is written,

"'I will strike the Shepherd,
and the sheep will be scattered.'

But after I'm raised up, I will go before you to the Galilee."

Peter said to Him, "Even though all fall away, I won't!"

And *Yeshua* said to him, "Amen, I tell you, today—this very night—before a rooster crows twice, you will deny Me three times."

But Peter kept insisting exceedingly, "Even if I must die with You, I'll never deny You!" And they all were saying the same.

Then they come to a place whose name is Gethsemane; and *Yeshua* says to His disciples, "Sit here while I pray."

He takes with Him Peter, Jacob, and John; and He began to be deeply distressed and troubled. And He tells them, "My soul is deeply grieved, even to the point of death. Stay here and keep watch."

Going a little farther, He fell to the ground and began praying that if possible this hour might pass Him by. And He was saying, "*Abba*, Father, all things are possible for You! Take this cup from Me! Yet not what I will, but what You will."

Then He comes and finds them sleeping; and He tells Peter, "Simon, you're asleep? Couldn't you keep watch for one hour? Keep watching and praying, so that you do not enter into temptation. The spirit is willing, but the flesh is weak."

Again He went away and prayed, saying the same words. And again He came and found them sleeping, for their eyes were very heavy. They didn't know what to answer Him.

And He comes the third time and says to them, "Are you still sleeping and taking your rest? Enough! The hour has come. Look, the Son of Man is being delivered into the hands of sinners. Get up, let's go! Look, My betrayer is near."

Right away, while *Yeshua* was still speaking, Judah comes up, one of the Twelve, and with him a crowd with swords and clubs, from the ruling *kohanim*, *Torah* scholars, and elders. Now His betrayer had given them a signal, saying, "The One I kiss, He's the One! Seize Him and lead Him away under guard."

As soon as Judah came, he drew near to *Yeshua* and said, "Rabbi!" and kissed Him. Then they threw their hands on *Yeshua* and seized Him.

Mark 14:27-46

Then they led *Yeshua* away to the *kohen gadol*. And all the ruling *kohanim*, elders, and *Torah* scholars gathered. Peter had followed Him from a distance, right into the courtyard of the *kohen gadol*. He was sitting with the guards, warming himself by the fire.

Now the ruling *kohanim* and all the Sanhedrin kept trying to get evidence against *Yeshua* so they could put Him to death, but they weren't finding any.

Mark 14:53-55

Now they had lit a fire in the center of the courtyard and sat down together, and Peter was sitting among them. Then a servant girl saw him sitting at the fire. She looked straight at him and said, "This one was with Him too!"

But he denied it, saying, "Woman, I don't know Him!"

A little later, another saw him and said, "You, too, are one of them."

But Peter said, "Man, I am not!"

And about an hour later, another began to insist, saying, "Certainly this fellow was with Him, for he too is a Galilean!"

But Peter said, "Man, I don't know what you're talking about!" And immediately, while he was still speaking, a rooster crowed. And the Lord turned and looked straight at Peter.

Then Peter remembered the word of the Lord, how He had told him, 'Before the rooster crows today, you will deny Me three times.'

And Peter went out and wept bitterly.

Luke 22:55-62

Now the ruling *kohanim* and all the Sanhedrin kept trying to get evidence against *Yeshua* so they could put Him to death, but they weren't finding any. Many were giving false testimony against Him, but their testimony wasn't consistent.

Some stood up and began to give false testimony against Him, saying, "We heard Him say, 'I will destroy this Temple made with hands, and in three days I will build another made without hands.'" Yet even then, their testimony didn't agree.

Mark 14:55-59

Right at daybreak, the ruling *kohanim* held a meeting to consult with the elders and *Torah* scholars and the whole Sanhedrin. They tied up *Yeshua*, led Him away, and handed Him over to Pilate.

Mark 15:1

Now *Yeshua* stood before the governor. The governor questioned Him, saying, "Are You the King of the Jews?"

"You say so," *Yeshua* said. And while He was accused by the ruling *kohanim* and elders, He did not answer.

Then Pilate said to Him, "Don't You hear how many things they testify against you?" *Yeshua* did not answer, not even one word, so the governor was greatly amazed.

Now during the feast, the governor was accustomed to release to the crowd one prisoner, anyone they wanted. At that time they had a notorious prisoner, called *Yeshua Bar-Abba*. So when they were gathered together,

Pilate said to them, "Which one do you want me to release for you? *Yeshua* who is *Bar-Abba*, or *Yeshua* who is called Messiah?" For he knew that they had handed Him over out of envy. While Pilate was sitting on the judgment seat, his wife sent him a message, saying, "Don't have anything to do with that righteous Man, for today I've suffered many things in a dream because of Him."

Now the ruling *kohanim* and elders persuaded the crowds that they should ask for *Bar-Abba* and destroy *Yeshua*. But the governor responded, "Which of the two do you want me to release for you?"

And they said, "*Bar-Abba!*"

Pilate said to them, "What then shall I do with *Yeshua*, who is called Messiah?"

"Execute Him!" all of them say.

But Pilate said, "Why? What evil has He done?"

But they kept shouting all the more, saying, "Let Him be executed!"

When Pilate saw he was accomplishing nothing, but instead a riot was starting, he took some water and washed his hands in front of the crowd. "I am innocent of this blood," he said. "You see to it yourselves!"

All the people answered and said, "His blood be on us and on our children!" Then he released to them *Bar-Abba*. And after he had *Yeshua* scourged, he handed Him over to be crucified. Then the governor's soldiers took *Yeshua* into the Praetorium and gathered the whole cohort around Him. They stripped Him and put a scarlet robe around Him. And after braiding a crown of thorns, they placed it on His head and put a staff in His right hand. And falling on their knees before Him, they mocked Him, saying, "Hail, King of the Jews!" They spat on Him, and they took the staff and beat Him over and over on the head. When they finished mocking Him, they stripped the robe off Him and put His own clothes back on Him. And they led Him away to crucify Him.

Matthew 27:11-31

When they finished mocking Him, they stripped the purple off Him and put His own clothes back on Him.

And they led Him out to crucify Him.

From Mark 15:20 TLV ©2018, image #43/54

44. God Provides the Lamb

Now Simon of Cyrene, the father of Alexander and Rufus, was coming in from the countryside. The soldiers force this passerby to carry *Yeshua*'s crossbeam. They bring *Yeshua* to the place called Golgotha (which is translated, Place of a Skull).

Mark 15:21-22

Others, two evildoers, were also led away to be put to death with Him. When they came to the place called the Skull, there they crucified Him and the evildoers, one on His right and the other on His left.

But *Yeshua* was saying, "Father, forgive them, for they do not know what they are doing." Then they cast lots, dividing up His clothing.

Luke 23:32-34a

Pilate also wrote a sign and put it on the execution stake. It was written, "*YESHUA HA-NATZRATI,* THE KING OF THE JEWS." Many Judeans read this sign, because the place where *Yeshua* was executed was near the city; it was written in Hebrew, Latin, and Greek.

The ruling *kohanim* of the Judeans were saying to Pilate, "Don't write, 'The King of the Jews,' but that He said, 'I am King of the Jews.'"

"What I have written, I have written," Pilate answered.

So the soldiers, when they executed *Yeshua*, took His outer garments and made four parts, a part for each soldier. They took His tunic also, but it was seamless, woven top to bottom in one piece. So they said to one another, "Let's not tear it, but cast lots for it to see whose it will be." This was so the Scripture would be fulfilled,

"They divided My garments among them,

and for My clothing they cast lots."

So the soldiers did these things.

Standing near the execution stake of *Yeshua* were His mother, His mother's sister, Miriam the wife of Clopas, and Miriam from Magdala. *Yeshua* saw His mother and the disciple whom He loved standing nearby. He tells His mother, "Woman, behold, your son!" Then He tells the disciple, "Behold, your mother!" From that very hour, the disciple took her into his own home.

John 19:19-27

The people stood there watching. And even the leaders were sneering at Him, saying, "He saved others; let Him save Himself if He is the Messiah of God, the Chosen One!"

The soldiers likewise mocked Him, coming up and bringing Him sour wine, and saying, "If You are the King of the Jews, save Yourself."

Luke 23:35-37

One of the evildoers hanging there was jeering at Him, saying, "Aren't You the Messiah? Save Yourself—and us!"

But the other one, rebuking him, replied, "Don't you fear God, since you are under the same sentence? We're getting what we deserve for our actions, and rightly so—but this One has done nothing wrong." And he said, "*Yeshua,* remember me when You come into Your kingdom."

Yeshua said to him, "Amen, I tell you, today you shall be with Me in Paradise."

Luke 23:39-43

Now from the sixth hour, darkness fell upon all the land until the ninth hour. About the ninth hour *Yeshua* cried out with a loud voice, saying, "*Eli, Eli, lema sabachthani?*" that is, "My God, My God, why have You abandoned Me?"

When some of those standing there heard it, they began saying, "This Man is calling for Elijah."

Matthew 27:45-47

After this, when *Yeshua* knew that all things were now completed, to fulfill the Scripture *He* said, "I am thirsty." A jar full of sour wine was sitting there, so they put a sponge soaked with the sour wine on a hyssop branch and brought it to His mouth. When *Yeshua* tasted the sour wine, He said, "It is finished!" And He bowed His head and gave up His spirit.

John 19:28-30

And behold, the curtain of the Temple was split in two, from top to bottom. And the earth quaked and rocks were split apart. And the tombs were opened, and many bodies of the *kedoshim* who were sleeping were raised to life. And coming forth out of the tombs after His resurrection, they went into the holy city and appeared to many.

Now the centurion, and those with him keeping guard over *Yeshua*, when they saw the earthquake and what was happening, they became terribly frightened and said, "This really was the Son of God!"

Many women were there, watching from a distance. They had followed *Yeshua* from the Galilee, serving Him. Among them were Miriam from Magdala, Miriam the mother of Jacob and Joseph, and the mother of Zebedee's sons.

Matthew 27:51-56

It was the Day of Preparation, and the next day was a festival *Shabbat*. So that the bodies should not remain on the execution stake during *Shabbat*, the Judean leaders asked Pilate to have the legs broken and to have the bodies taken away.

So the soldiers came and broke the legs of the first and then the other who had been executed with *Yeshua*. Now when they came to *Yeshua* and saw that He was already dead, they did not break His legs. But one of the soldiers pierced His side with a spear, and immediately blood and water came out. He who has seen it has testified, and his testimony is true. He knows that he is telling the truth, so that you also may believe.

These things happened so that the Scripture would be fulfilled, "Not a bone of His shall be broken." And again another Scripture says, "They shall look on Him whom they have pierced."

After these things, Joseph of Arimathea asked Pilate if he could take *Yeshua's* body away. Joseph was a disciple of *Yeshua*, but secretly for fear of the Judean leaders. Pilate gave permission, so Joseph came and took the body away. Nicodemus, who had first visited *Yeshua* at night, also came bringing a mixture of myrrh and aloes, about a hundred pounds. Then they took the body of *Yeshua* and wrapped it in linen with the spices, as is the Jewish burial custom.

Now in the place where He was executed, there was a garden. In the garden was a new tomb where no one had yet been buried. Because it was the Jewish Day of Preparation and the tomb was nearby, they laid *Yeshua* there.

John 19:31-42

Now on the next day, which is after the preparation, the ruling *kohanim* and Pharisees were gathered before Pilate.

"Sir," they said, "we remember how that deceiver said while He was still alive, 'After three days I'm to be raised.' Therefore, order the tomb to be made secure until the third day, so His disciples do not come and steal Him away. They will tell the people, 'He is risen from the dead,' and the last deception will be worse than the first!"

"You have a guard," Pilate said to them. "Go, make it as secure as you know how." So they went and made the tomb secure, sealing the stone along with the soldiers of the guard.

Matthew 27:62-66

The people stood there watching. And even the leaders were sneering at Him, saying,
"He saved others; let Him save Himself if He is the Messiah of God, the Chosen One!"
From Luke 23:35 TLV ©2018, image #44/54

45. God Saves the World

When *Shabbat* was over, Miriam of Magdala, Miriam the mother of Jacob, and Salome bought spices, so that they might come and anoint *Yeshua*'s body.

Mark 16:1

Now on the first day of the week, at daybreak, the women came to the tomb, carrying the spices they had prepared.

Luke 24:1

And suddenly there was a great earthquake, for an angel of ADONAI descended from heaven and came and rolled back the stone and sat on it. His appearance was like lightning, and his clothing as white as snow. And those keeping watch were shaken for fear of him and became like dead men.

But the angel answered and said to the women, "Do not be afraid, for I know you are looking for *Yeshua* who was crucified. He is not here; for He is risen, just as He said. Come, see the place where He was lying. Go quickly now and tell His disciples that He is risen from the dead. And behold, He's going before you to the Galilee. There you will see Him. See, I have told you!" They quickly left the tomb, with fear yet with great joy, and ran to bring news to His disciples.

And behold, *Yeshua* met them. "*Shalom!*" He said. They drew near, grasped his feet, and worshiped Him. "Don't be afraid," *Yeshua* said to them. "Go tell My brothers to head for the Galilee, and there they will see Me."

Matthew 28:2-10

But Miriam stood outside the tomb weeping. As she was weeping, she bent down to look into the tomb. She sees two angels in white sitting, one at the head and one at the feet, where *Yeshua*'s body had been lying.

"Woman, why are you crying?" they say to her.

She says to them, "Because they took away my Master, and I don't know where they've put Him." After she said these things, she turned around. And she sees *Yeshua* standing there. Yet she didn't know that it was *Yeshua*.

Yeshua says to her, "Woman, why are you weeping? Who are you looking for?"

Thinking He's the gardener, she says to Him, "Sir, if You've carried Him away, tell me where You've put Him, and I will take Him away."

Yeshua says to her, "Miriam!"

Turning around, she says to Him in Aramaic, "*Rabboni!*" (which means Teacher).

Yeshua says to her, "Stop clinging to Me, for I have not yet gone up to the Father. Go to My brothers and tell them, 'I am going up to My Father and your Father, to My God and your God.'"

Miriam from Magdala comes, announcing to the disciples, "I've seen the Lord," and what He had said to her.

John 20:11-8

And when they returned from the tomb, they told all these things to the eleven and to everyone else. Now it was Miriam from Magdala, Joanna, the Miriam of Jacob, and others together with them who were telling these things to the emissaries.

But these words appeared to them as nonsense, and they would not believe them. But Peter got up and ran to the tomb. Leaning in, he sees only the linen cloths. And he went away to his home, marveling at what had happened.

Now behold, two of them on that very day were traveling to a village named Emmaus, a distance of about seven miles from Jerusalem. They were speaking with one another about all the things that had been happening. While they were talking and discussing, *Yeshua* Himself approached and began traveling with them. But their eyes were kept from recognizing Him.

Then He said to them, "What are these things you are discussing with one another as you are walking along?"

They stood still, looking gloomy. Then the one named Cleopas answered and said to Him, "Are You the only one visiting Jerusalem who doesn't know the things that happened there in these days?"

Yeshua said to them, "What kind of things?"

And they said to Him, "The things about *Yeshua* from *Natzeret*, who was a Prophet, powerful in deed and word before God and all the people— how the ruling *kohanim* and our leaders handed Him over to be sentenced to death, and they executed Him. But we were hoping that He was the One about to redeem Israel. Besides all this, today is the third day since these things happened.

"But also some women among us amazed us. Early in the morning they were at the tomb. When they didn't find His body, they came saying that they had also seen a vision of angels, who said He is alive! Some of those with us went to the tomb and found it just as the women said, but they did not see Him."

Yeshua said to them, "Oh foolish ones, so slow of heart to put your trust in all that the prophets spoke! Was it not necessary for Messiah to suffer these things and to enter into His glory?" Then beginning with Moses and all the Prophets, He explained to them the things written about Himself in all the Scriptures.

They approached the village where they were going, and He acted as though He were going farther on. But they urged Him, saying, "Stay with us, for it is nearly evening and the day is already gone." So He went in to stay with them.

And it happened that when He was reclining at the table with them, He took the *matzah*, offered a *bracha* and, breaking it, gave it to them. Then their eyes were opened and they recognized Him, and He disappeared from them.

They said to one another, "Didn't our heart burn within us while He was speaking with us on the road, while He was explaining the Scriptures to us?" And they got up that very hour and returned to Jerusalem. They found the eleven and others with them gathered together, saying, "The Lord is risen indeed! He has appeared to Simon!" Then they began telling about the events on the road and how He became recognized by them in the breaking of the *matzah*.

While they were speaking of these things, *Yeshua* Himself stood in the midst of them and said, "*Shalom Aleichem!*" But they were startled and terrified, thinking they were seeing a ghost.

Then He said to them, "Why are you so shaken? And why do doubts arise in your heart? Look at My hands and My feet—it is I Myself! Touch Me and see! For a spirit doesn't have flesh and bones, as you see I have." And when He had said this, He showed them His hands and His feet.

But while they were still in disbelief due to joy and wonder, He said to them, "Do you have anything to eat here?"

They gave Him a piece of broiled fish, and He took it and ate it in their presence.

Then He said to them, "These are My words which I spoke to you while I was still with you—everything written concerning Me in the *Torah* of Moses and the Prophets and the Psalms must be fulfilled."

Then He opened their minds to understand the Scriptures, and He said to them, "So it is written, that the Messiah is to suffer and to rise from the dead on the third day, and that repentance for the removal of sins is to be proclaimed in His name to all nations, beginning from Jerusalem. You are witnesses of these things.

Luke 24:9-48

Yeshua says to her, "Miriam!" Turning around, she says to Him in Aramaic, "*Rabboni!*" (which means Teacher).

From John 20:16 TLV ©2018, image #45/54

46. God Forgives Unbelief

One of the Twelve, Thomas called the Twin, was not with them when *Yeshua* came. The other disciples were saying to him, "We've seen the Lord!"

But he replied to them, "Unless I see the nail prints in His hands, and put my finger into the mark of the nails, and put my hand in His side, I will never believe!"

Eight days later the disciples were again inside, and Thomas was with them. *Yeshua* comes, despite the locked doors. He stood in their midst and said, *"Shalom aleichem!"* Then He said to Thomas, "Put your finger here, and look at My hands. Reach out your hand and put it into My side. Stop doubting and believe!"

Thomas answered and said to Him, "My Lord and my God!"

Yeshua said to Him, "Because you have seen Me, you have believed? Blessed are the ones who have not seen and yet have believed!"

Yeshua performed many other signs in the presence of the disciples, which are not written in this book. But these things have been written so that you may believe that *Yeshua* is *Mashiach Ben-Elohim*, and that by believing you may have life in His name.

John 20:24-31

After these things, *Yeshua* revealed Himself again to the disciples at the Sea of Tiberias. Now here is how He appeared. Simon Peter, Thomas called the Twin, Nathanael of Cana in the Galilee, the sons of Zebedee, and two of the other disciples were together.

Simon Peter said to them, "I'm going fishing."

"We're coming with you too," they said. They went out and got into the boat, and that night they caught nothing.

At dawn, *Yeshua* stood on the beach; but the disciples didn't know that it was *Yeshua*. So *Yeshua* said to them, "Boys, you don't happen to have any fish, do you?"

"No," they answered Him.

He said to them, "Throw the net off the right side of the boat, and you'll find some." So they threw the net, and they were not able to haul it in because of the great number of fish.

Therefore, the disciple whom *Yeshua* loved said to Peter, "It's the Lord!" When Simon Peter heard that it was the Lord, he tied his outer garment around himself—for he was stripped down for work—and threw himself into the sea. But the other disciples came in the boat from about two hundred cubits offshore, dragging the net full of fish.

So when they got out onto the land, they saw a charcoal fire with fish placed on it, and bread. *Yeshua* said to them, "Bring some of the fish you've just caught." Simon Peter went aboard and hauled the net to shore. There were 153 fish, many of them big; but the net was not broken. *Yeshua* said to them, "Come, have breakfast." None of the disciples dared ask Him, "Who are You?"—knowing it was the Lord. *Yeshua* comes and takes the bread and gives it to them, and likewise the fish. This was now the third time that *Yeshua* was revealed to the disciples after He was raised from the dead.

When they had finished breakfast, *Yeshua* said to Simon Peter, "Simon, son of John, do you love Me more than these?"

"Yes, Lord," he said to Him, "You know that I love you."

He said to him, "Feed My lambs!"

He said to him again a second time, "Simon, son of John, do you love Me?"

"Yes, Lord," he said, "You know that I love You."

He said to him, "Take care of My sheep!"

He said to him a third time, "Simon, son of John, do you love Me?"

Peter was grieved because He said to him for a third time, "Do you love Me?" And he said to Him, "Lord, You know everything! You know that I love You!"

Yeshua said to him, "Feed My sheep!"

"Amen, amen I tell you, when you were younger, you used to dress yourself and walk wherever you wanted; but when you grow old, you will stretch out your hands, and someone else will dress you and carry you where you do not want to go."

Now this He said to indicate by what kind of death Peter was going to glorify God.

And after this, *Yeshua* said to him, "Follow Me!"

Peter, turning around, sees the disciple following. This was the one whom *Yeshua* loved, who also had reclined against *Yeshua's* chest at the *seder* meal and said, "Master, who is the one who is betraying You?"

Seeing him, Peter said to *Yeshua*, "Lord, what about him?"

Yeshua said to him, "If I want him to remain until I come, what is that to you? You follow Me!"

Therefore this saying went out among the brothers and sisters, that this disciple would not die.

Yet *Yeshua* did not say to him that he would not die, but, "If I want him to remain until I come, what is that to you?"

This is the disciple who is an eyewitness of these things and wrote these things. We know that his testimony is true. There are also many other things that *Yeshua* did. If all of them were to be written one by one, I suppose that not even the world itself will have room for the books being written!

John 21:1-25

Now the eleven disciples went to the Galilee, to the mountain *Yeshua* had designated. When they saw Him, they worshiped; but some wavered.

And *Yeshua* came up to them and spoke to them, saying, "All authority in heaven and on earth has been given to Me.

Go therefore and make disciples of all nations, immersing them in the name of the Father and the Son and the *Ruach ha-Kodesh*, teaching them to observe all I have commanded you. And remember! I am with you always, even to the end of the age."

Matthew 28:16-20

Therefore, the disciple whom *Yeshua* loved said to Peter, "It's the Lord!" When Simon Peter heard that it was the Lord, he tied his outer garment around himself—for he was stripped down for work—and threw himself into the sea.

From John 21:7 TLV ©2018, image #46/54

47. God Lifts *Yeshua* Up

Who has believed our report?

To whom is the arm of ADONAI revealed?

For He grew up before Him

like a tender shoot,

    like a root out of dry ground.

He had no form or majesty

that we should look at Him,

nor beauty that we should desire Him.

He was despised and rejected by men,

a man of sorrows, acquainted with grief,

One from whom people hide their faces.

He was despised,

and we did not esteem Him.

Surely He has borne our griefs

    and carried our pains.

Yet we esteemed Him stricken,

    struck by God, and afflicted.

But He was pierced

    because of our transgressions,

crushed because of our iniquities.

The chastisement for our *shalom*

was upon Him,

and by His stripes we are healed.

We all like sheep have gone astray.

Each of us turned to his own way.

So ADONAI has laid on Him

the iniquity of us all.

He was oppressed and He was afflicted

yet He did not open His mouth.

Like a lamb led to the slaughter,

like a sheep before its shearers is silent,

so He did not open His mouth.

Because of oppression and judgment

He was taken away.

As for His generation, who considered?

For He was cut off from

the land of the living,

for the transgression of my people—

the stroke was theirs.

His grave was given with the wicked,

and by a rich man in His death,

though He had done no violence,

nor was there any deceit in His mouth.

Yet it pleased ADONAI to bruise Him.

He caused Him to suffer.

If He makes His soul a guilt offering,

He will see His offspring,

He will prolong His days,

and the will of ADONAI

will succeed by His hand.

As a result of the anguish of His soul

He will see it and be satisfied

by His knowledge.

The Righteous One, My Servant

will make many righteous

    and He will bear their iniquities.

Therefore I will give Him a portion with the
great,

and He will divide the spoil

with the mighty—

because He poured out His soul to death,

    and was counted with transgressors.

For He bore the sin of many,

    and interceded for the transgressors.

Isaiah 53:1-12

189

To them He showed Himself to be alive after His suffering through many convincing proofs, appearing to them for 40 days and speaking about the kingdom of God.

Now while staying with them, He commanded them not to leave Jerusalem, but to wait for what the Father promised—which, He said, "You heard from Me. For John immersed with water, but you will be immersed in the *Ruach ha-Kodesh* not many days from now."

So when they gathered together, they asked Him, "Lord, are You restoring the kingdom to Israel at this time?"

He said to them, "It is not your place to know the times or seasons which the Father has placed under His own control. But you will receive power when the *Ruach ha-Kodesh* has come upon you; and you will be My witnesses in Jerusalem, and through all Judah, and Samaria, and to the end of the earth."

After saying all this—while they were watching—He was taken up, and a cloud received Him out of their sight. While they were staring into heaven as He went up, suddenly two men stood with them in white clothing. They said, "Men of Galilee, why do you keep standing here staring into heaven? This *Yeshua*, who was taken up from you into heaven, will come in the same way as you saw Him go into heaven."

Then they returned to Jerusalem from the Mount of Olives (which is near Jerusalem, a *Shabbat* day's journey). When they had entered, they went up to the upper room where they were staying—Peter and John and Jacob and Andrew; Philip and Thomas, Bartholomew and Matthew; Jacob son of Alphaeus and Simon the Zealot and Judah son of Jacob. All these with one mind were continuing together in prayer—along with the women and Miriam, *Yeshua*'s mother, and His brothers.

In those days, Peter stood up among the brothers and sisters (the number of names all together was about 120) and said, "Brothers, the Scripture had to be fulfilled, which the *Ruach ha-Kodesh* foretold by the mouth of David, concerning Judah—who became a guide to those who seized *Yeshua*. For he was counted among us and received his share of this office."

Acts 1:3-17

So they nominated two—Joseph, called Barsabbas (also called Justus), and Matthias. And they prayed and said, "You, O Lord, who knows the hearts of all men, show us which of these two You have chosen to take the position in this office as emissary, from which Judah turned aside to go to his own place."

Then they cast lots for them, and the lot fell upon Matthias; and he was added to the eleven emissaries.

Acts 1:23-26

After saying all this—while they were watching—He was taken up,
and a cloud received Him out of their sight.

From Acts 1:9 TLV ©2018, image #47/54

191

48. God Gives His Spirit

When the day of *Shavuot* had come, they were all together in one place. Suddenly there came from heaven a sound like a mighty rushing wind, and it filled the whole house where they were sitting. And tongues like fire spreading out appeared to them and settled on each one of them. They were all filled with the *Ruach ha-Kodesh* and began to speak in other tongues as the *Ruach* enabled them to speak out.

Now Jewish people were staying in Jerusalem, devout men from every nation under heaven. And when this sound came, the crowd gathered. They were bewildered, because each was hearing them speaking in his own language. And they were amazed and astonished, saying, "All these who are speaking—aren't they Galileans? How is it that we each hear our own birth language? Parthians and Medes and Elamites and those living in Mesopotamia, Judea and Cappadocia, Pontus and Asia, Phrygia and Pamphylia, Egypt and parts of Libya toward Cyrene, and visitors from Rome (both Jewish people and proselytes), Cretans and Arabs—we hear them declaring in our own tongues the mighty deeds of God!" And they were all amazed and perplexed, saying to each other, "What does this mean?"

Others, poking fun, were saying, "They are full of sweet new wine!"

But Peter, standing with the Eleven, raised his voice and addressed them: "Fellow Judeans and all who are staying in Jerusalem, let this be known to you, and pay attention to my words. These men are not drunk, as you suppose—for it's only the third hour of the day! But this is what was spoken about through the prophet Joel:

"'And it shall be in the last days,' says God,

'that I will pour out My *Ruach* on all flesh.

Your sons and your daughters shall Prophesy,

your young men shall see visions,

and your old men shall dream dreams.

Even on My slaves, male and female,

I will pour out My *Ruach* in those days,

and they shall prophesy.

Acts 2:1-18

"Men of Israel, hear these words! *Yeshua ha-Natzrati*—a Man authenticated to you by God with mighty deeds and wonders and signs God performed through Him in your midst, as you yourselves know— this *Yeshua*, given over by God's predetermined plan and foreknowledge, nailed to the cross by the hands of lawless men, you killed. But God raised Him up, releasing Him from the pains of death, since it was impossible for Him to be held by it. For David says about Him,

'I saw ADONAI always before me,

for He is at my right hand

so that I might not be shaken.

Therefore my heart was glad

and my tongue rejoiced;

moreover, my body also will live in hope,

because You will not abandon my soul to *Sheol* or let Your Holy One see decay.

You have made known to me the paths of
life;

You will fill me with joy in Your presence.'

"Brothers, I can confidently tell you that
the patriarch David died and was buried—his
tomb is with us to this day. So because he was a
prophet and knew God had sworn with an oath
to him to seat one of his descendants on his
throne, David saw beforehand and spoke of
Messiah's resurrection—that He was not
abandoned to *Sheol*, and His body did not see
decay.

"This *Yeshua* God raised up—we all are
witnesses! Therefore, being exalted to the right
hand of God and receiving from the Father the
promise of the *Ruach ha-Kodesh*, He poured out
this—what you now see and hear.

For David did not ascend into the
heavens; yet he himself says,

"'*ADONAI* said to my Lord,

"Sit at my right hand,

until I make Your enemies a footstool

for Your feet."'

"Therefore let the whole house of Israel
know for certain that God has made Him—this
Yeshua whom you had crucified—both Lord and
Messiah!"

Now when they heard this, they were cut
to the heart and said to Peter and the rest of the
emissaries, "Fellow brethren, what shall we do?"

Peter said to them, "Repent, and let each
of you be immersed in the name of Messiah
Yeshua for the removal of your sins, and you will
receive the gift of the *Ruach ha-Kodesh*. For the
promise is for you and your children, and for all
who are far away—as many as *ADONAI* our God
calls to Himself."

With many other words he warned them
and kept urging them, saying, "Save yourselves
from this twisted generation!"

So those who received his message were
immersed, and that day about three thousand
souls were added.

They were devoting themselves to the
teaching of the emissaries and to fellowship, to
breaking bread, and to prayers. Fear lay upon
every soul, and many wonders and signs were
happening through the emissaries.

And all who believed were together,
having everything in common. They began
selling their property and possessions and
sharing them with all, as any had need. Day by
day they continued with one mind, spending
time at the Temple, and breaking bread from
house to house. They were sharing meals with
gladness and sincerity of heart, praising God, and
having favor with all the people.

And every day the Lord was adding to
their number those being saved.

Acts 2:22-47

Suddenly there came from heaven a sound like a mighty rushing wind, and it filled the whole house where they were sitting. And tongues like fire spreading out appeared to them and settled on each one of them. They were all filled with the *Ruach ha-Kodesh* and began to speak in other tongues as the *Ruach* enabled them to speak out.

From Acts 2:2-4 TLV ©2018, image #48/54

49. God Opens Blind Eyes

The word of God kept on spreading, and the number of disciples in Jerusalem greatly multiplied; even a great number of the *kohanim* were becoming obedient to the faith.

Now Stephen, full of grace and power, was doing great wonders and signs among the people. But some men from what was called the Synagogue of the Freedmen—both Cyrenians and Alexandrians, as well as some from Cilicia and Asia—stood up and began arguing with Stephen. But they could not withstand the wisdom and the *Ruach* by whom he was speaking.

Then they secretly instigated men into saying, "We have heard him speaking blasphemous words against Moses and against God!" They also incited the people, the elders, and the *Torah* scholars; and they rushed at Stephen, seized him, and led him away to the Sanhedrin. They set up false witnesses who said, "This man never stops speaking words against this holy place and the *Torah*. For we have heard him saying that this *Yeshua ha-Natzrati* will destroy this place and change the customs that Moses handed down to us." Watching him intently, everyone who was sitting in the Sanhedrin saw that his face was like the face of an angel.

Acts 6:7-15

Now Saul was in agreement with Stephen's execution. On that day a great persecution arose against Messiah's community in Jerusalem, and they were all scattered throughout the region of Judea and Samaria, except the emissaries. Some devout men buried Stephen and mourned deeply for him.

But Saul was destroying Messiah's community, entering house after house; and dragging off men and women, he was throwing them into prison.

Acts 8:1-3

Now Saul, still breathing out threats and murder against the Lord's disciples, went to the *kohen gadol*. He requested letters of introduction from him to the synagogues in Damascus, so that if he found any men or women belonging to the Way, he might bring them as prisoners to Jerusalem.

As he was traveling, approaching Damascus, suddenly a light from heaven flashed around him. Falling to the ground, he heard a voice saying to him, "Saul, Saul, why are you persecuting Me?"

"Who are You, Lord?" Saul said.

"I am *Yeshua*—whom you are persecuting. But get up and go into the city, and you will be told what you must do."

The men traveling with him stood speechless, hearing the voice but seeing no one. Saul got up from the ground—but opening his eyes, he could see nothing. They led him by the hand and brought him into Damascus. For three days he could not see, and he did not eat or drink.

Now there was a disciple named Ananias in Damascus. The Lord said to him, "Ananias."

He said, "Here I am, Lord."

The Lord said to him, "Get up and go to the street named Straight, and ask in the house of Judah for someone from Tarsus named Saul.

For look, he is praying; and in a vision he has seen a man named Ananias coming in and laying his hands on him, so that he might regain his sight."

But Ananias answered, "Lord, I have heard from many about this man—how much harm he has done to your *kedoshim* in Jerusalem. And here he has authority from the ruling *kohanim* to tie up all who call on Your name."

But the Lord said to him, "Go, for he is a choice instrument to carry My name before nations and kings and *Bnei-Yisrael*. For I will show him how much he must suffer for My name's sake."

So Ananias left and entered into the house. Laying hands on Saul, he said, "Brother Saul, the Lord—*Yeshua*, the One who appeared to you on the road by which you were coming—has sent me, so that you might regain your sight and be filled with the *Ruach ha-Kodesh*."

Immediately, something like scales fell from Saul's eyes, and he regained his sight. Then he got up and was immersed; and when he had taken food, he was strengthened.

Now for several days, he was with the disciples in Damascus. Immediately he began proclaiming *Yeshua* in the synagogues, saying, "He is *Ben-Elohim*."

All those hearing him were amazed. They were saying, "Isn't this the one who made havoc in Jerusalem for all those who call on this name? And hasn't he come here to bring them as prisoners before the ruling *kohanim*?"

But Saul kept growing stronger, and he was confounding the Jewish people living in Damascus by proving that *Yeshua* is the Messiah. When many days had passed, these Jewish people plotted to kill him— but their plot became known to Saul. They were watching the gates day and night, to kill him.

But the disciples took Saul by night and let him down over the wall, lowering him in a basket.

When Saul arrived in Jerusalem, he made attempts to join up with the disciples—but they were all afraid of him, not believing that he was a disciple. But Barnabas took him in and brought him to the emissaries. He described to them how Saul had seen the Lord on the road and the Lord had spoken to him, and how he had spoken boldly in the name of *Yeshua*.

So Saul was with them, going in and out in Jerusalem, speaking boldly in the name of the Lord. He was speaking and arguing with the Hellenists, but they were trying to kill him. When the brothers found out, they brought him down to Caesarea and sent him off to Tarsus.

So Messiah's community throughout all Judea and Galilee and Samaria had *shalom* and was built up. Walking in the fear of the Lord and in the comfort of the *Ruach ha-Kodesh*, it kept multiplying.

Acts 9:1-31

As he was traveling, approaching Damascus, suddenly a light from heaven flashed around him. Falling to the ground, he heard a voice saying to him, "Saul, Saul, why are you persecuting Me?"

From Acts 9:3-4 TLV ©2018, image #49/54

50. God Frees the Captives

Now those scattered because of the persecution that happened in connection with Stephen traveled as far as Phoenicia and Cyprus and Antioch, telling the message only to Judeans. However, there were some of them, men of Cyprus and Cyrene, who came to Antioch and began speaking to the Hellenists also, proclaiming the Lord *Yeshua*. The hand of the Lord was with them, and a great number who believed turned to the Lord.

News about these things reached the ears of the community in Jerusalem, and they sent Barnabas to Antioch. When he arrived and saw the grace of God, he was thrilled. He encouraged them all to remain true to the Lord with heartfelt devotion. For Barnabas was a good man, full of the *Ruach ha-Kodesh* and faith. And a large number was added to the Lord.

Then Barnabas left for Tarsus to look for Saul, and when he had found him, he brought him to Antioch. For a whole year they met together with Messiah's community and taught a large number. Now it was in Antioch that the disciples were first called "Christianoi."

Acts 11:19-26

Now in the Antioch community, there were prophets and teachers: Barnabas, Simeon called Niger, Lucius the Cyrenian, Manaen (brought up since childhood with Herod the Tetrarch), and Saul.

While they were serving the Lord and fasting, the *Ruach ha-Kodesh* said, "Set apart for me Barnabas and Saul for the work to which I have called them." Then after fasting, praying, and laying hands on them, they sent them off.

So, sent out by the *Ruach ha-Kodesh*, they went down to Seleucia, and from there they sailed to Cyprus. When they arrived at Salamis, they began to proclaim the word of God in the Jewish synagogues. They also had John as a helper.

When they had gone throughout the whole island as far as Paphos, they found a man who was a magician—a Jewish false prophet, whose name was Bar-Yeshua. He was with the proconsul, Sergius Paulus, an intelligent man. This man summoned Barnabas and Saul and sought to hear the word of God.

But Elymas the magician (for so his name is translated) was opposing them, seeking to turn the proconsul away from the faith. But Saul, who is also Paul, filled with the *Ruach ha-Kodesh*, fixed his gaze on him and said, "O you, full of all deceit and trickery, son of the devil, enemy of all righteousness—will you not stop making crooked the straight paths of the Lord?

Acts 13:1-10

Now a vision appeared to Paul in the night. A man from Macedonia was standing and pleading with him, saying, "Come over to Macedonia and help us!"

As soon as he had seen the vision, immediately we tried to go to Macedonia, concluding that God had called us to proclaim the Good News to them.

Acts 16:9-10

It so happened that as we were going to prayer, we met a slave girl who had a spirit of divination, who was bringing her masters much profit from her fortune-telling.

Following after Paul and us, she kept shouting, saying, "These men are servants of *El Elyon*, who are proclaiming to you the way of salvation." She kept doing this for many days.

But Paul was irritated and turned and said to the spirit, "I command you in the name of Messiah *Yeshua* to come out of her!" And it came out of her that very moment.

But when her masters saw that the hope of profit was gone, they grabbed Paul and Silas and dragged them into the marketplace before the authorities.

And when they brought them to the chief authorities, they said, "These men are throwing our city into an uproar! Being Jewish, they advocate customs which are not permitted for us to accept or practice, being Romans."

Then the crowd joined in the attack on them. So the chief authorities ripped their clothes off them and commanded them to be beaten with rods. After inflicting many blows on them, they threw them into prison, ordering the jailer to guard them securely. Having received this charge, he threw them into the inner prison and fastened their feet in the stocks.

But about midnight, Paul and Silas were praying and singing hymns to God, and the prisoners were listening to them. Suddenly there was such a great earthquake that the foundations of the prison were shaken. Immediately all the doors were unlocked, and everyone's chains came loose.

When the jailer woke up and saw the prison doors opened, he drew his sword and was about to kill himself, supposing the prisoners had escaped.

But Paul cried out with a loud voice, saying, "Don't harm yourself! We're all here!"

The jailer called for lights and rushed in; and trembling with fear, he fell down before Paul and Silas. After he brought them out, he said, "Sirs, what must I do to be saved?"

They said, "Put your trust in the Lord *Yeshua* and you will be saved—you and your household!"

Then they spoke the word of the Lord to him, along with everyone in his household. He took them that very hour and washed their wounds, and at once he was immersed—he and all his household. The jailer brought them to his house and set food before them, and he was overjoyed that he with his entire household had put their trust in God.

When day came, the chief authorities sent their police officers, saying, "Release those men."

But the jailer reported these words to Paul, saying, "The chief authorities have sent orders to release you. So come out now, and go in *shalom*."

But Paul said to the officers, "They have beaten us publicly without a trial—men who are Roman citizens—and have thrown us into prison. And now they are sending us away secretly? No! Let them come themselves and lead us out!"

The police officers reported these words to the chief authorities. They became afraid when they heard they were Romans, so they came and apologized to them. After they escorted them out, they kept begging them to leave the city.

Acts 16:16-39

But about midnight, Paul and Silas were praying and singing hymns to God, and the prisoners were listening to them.
Suddenly there was such a great earthquake that the foundations of the prison were shaken.
Immediately all the doors were unlocked, and everyone's chains came loose.
From Acts 19:25-26 TLV ©2018, image #50/54

203

51. God is Our Salvation

Brothers and sisters, my heart's desire and my prayer to God for Israel is for their salvation.

Romans 10:1

For Messiah is the goal of the *Torah* as a means to righteousness for everyone who keeps trusting.

Romans 10:4

But what does it say?
  "The word is near you,
    in your mouth and in your heart,"
—that is, the word of faith that we are proclaiming:
  "For if you confess with your mouth
      that *Yeshua* is Lord,
  and believe in your heart
      that God raised Him from the dead,
    you will be saved.
  For with the heart
  it is believed for righteousness,
  and with the mouth
  it is confessed for salvation."

For the Scripture says, "Whoever trusts in Him will not be put to shame." For there is no distinction between Jew and Greek, for the same Lord is Lord of all—richly generous to all who call on Him. For "Everyone who calls upon the name of ADONAI shall be saved."

How then shall they call on the One in whom they have not trusted? And how shall they trust in the One they have not heard of? And how shall they hear without someone proclaiming? And how shall they proclaim unless they are sent? As it is written, "How beautiful are the feet of those who proclaim good news of good things!" But not all heeded the Good News.

For Isaiah says, "ADONAI, who has believed our report?" So faith comes from hearing, and hearing by the word of Messiah.

Romans 10:8-17

I say then, God has not rejected His people, has He? May it never be! For I too am an Israelite, of the seed of Abraham, of the tribe of Benjamin. God has not rejected His people whom He knew beforehand. Or do you not know what the Scripture says about Elijah, how he pleads with God against Israel?

"ADONAI, they have killed your prophets, they have destroyed your altars; I alone am left, and they are seeking my life."

But what is the divine response to him? "I have kept for Myself seven thousand men who have not bowed the knee to Baal."

So in the same way also at this present time there has come to be a remnant according to God's gracious choice. But if it is by grace, it is no longer by works; otherwise grace would no longer be grace.

Romans 11:1-6

I say then, they did not stumble so as to fall, did they? May it never be! But by their false step salvation has come to the Gentiles, to provoke Israel to jealousy. Now if their transgression leads to riches for the world, and their loss riches for the Gentiles, then how much more their fullness!

But I am speaking to you who are Gentiles. Insofar as I am an emissary to the Gentiles, I spotlight my ministry if somehow I might provoke to jealousy my own flesh and blood and save some of them. For if their rejection leads to the reconciliation of the world, what will their acceptance be but life from the dead?

But if some of the branches were broken off and you—being a wild olive—were grafted in among them and became a partaker of the root of the olive tree with its richness, do not boast against the branches. But if you do boast, it is not you who support the root but the root supports you.

You will say then, "Branches were broken off so that I might be grafted in." True enough. They were broken off because of unbelief, and you stand by faith. Do not be arrogant, but fear— for if God did not spare the natural branches, neither will He spare you. Notice then the kindness and severity of God:

severity toward those who fell;

but God's kindness toward you,

if you continue in His kindness;

otherwise you too will be cut off!

And they also,

if they do not continue in their unbelief,

will be grafted in;

for God is able to graft them in again.

For if you were cut out of that which by nature is a wild olive tree, and grafted contrary to nature into a cultivated olive tree, how much more will these natural branches be grafted into their own olive tree?

For I do not want you, brothers and sisters, to be ignorant of this mystery—lest you be wise in your own eyes—that a partial hardening has come upon Israel until the fullness of the Gentiles has come in; and in this way all Israel will be saved, as it is written,

"The Deliverer shall come out of Zion.

He shall turn away ungodliness from Jacob.

And this is My covenant with them,

when I take away their sins."

Concerning the Good News, they are hostile for your sake; but concerning chosenness, they are loved on account of the fathers— for the gifts and the calling of God are irrevocable. For just as you once were disobedient to God but now have been shown mercy because of their disobedience, in like manner these also have now been disobedient with the result that, because of the mercy shown to you, they also may receive mercy. For God has shut up all in disobedience, so that He might show mercy to all.

O the depth of the riches,

both of the wisdom and knowledge of God!

How unsearchable are His judgments

and how incomprehensible His ways!

For "who has known the mind of ADONAI,

or who has been His counselor?"

Or "who has first given to Him,

that it shall be repaid to him?"

For from Him and through Him and to Him are all things. To Him be the glory forever! Amen.

Romans 11:11-36

For if you were cut out of that which by nature is a wild olive tree, and grafted contrary to nature into a cultivated olive tree,
how much more will these natural branches be grafted into their own olive tree?

From Romans 11:24 TLV ©2018, image #51/54

52. God Heals Our Family Tree

If I speak with the tongues of men
and of angels
but have not love,
    I have become a noisy gong
    or a clanging cymbal.
If I have the gift of prophecy
and know all mysteries and all knowledge,
and if I have all faith so
as to remove mountains
but have not love,
    I am nothing.
If I give away all that I own
and if I hand over my body so I might boast
but have not love,
    I gain nothing.
Love is patient,
love is kind,
it does not envy,
it does not brag,
it is not puffed up,
it does not behave inappropriately,
it does not seek its own way,
it is not provoked,
it keeps no account of wrong,
it does not rejoice over injustice
    but rejoices in the truth;
it bears all things,
it believes all things,
it hopes all things,
it endures all things.
Love never fails—
but where there are prophecies,
    they will pass away;

where there are tongues,
    they will cease;
where there is knowledge,
    it will pass away.
For we know in part
and we prophesy in part;
but when that which is perfect has come,
    then that which is partial will pass away.
When I was a child,
    I spoke like a child,
    I thought like a child,
    I reasoned like a child.
When I became a man,
    I put away childish things.
For now we see in a mirror dimly,
    but then face to face.
Now I know in part,
    but then I will know fully,
    even as I have been fully known.
But now these three remain—
    faith, hope, and love.
    And the greatest of these is love.

1 Corinthians 13

Blessed be the God and Father of our Lord *Yeshua* the Messiah, who has blessed us with every spiritual blessing in the heavenly places in Messiah. He chose us in the Messiah before the foundation of the world, to be holy and blameless before Him in love. He predestined us for adoption as sons through Messiah *Yeshua*, in keeping with the good pleasure of His will— to the glorious praise of His grace, with which He favored us through the One He loves!

In Him we have redemption through His blood—the removal of trespasses—in keeping with the richness of His grace that He lavished on us. In all wisdom and insight, He made known to us the mystery of His will, in keeping with His good pleasure that He planned in Messiah.

The plan of the fullness of times is to bring all things together in the Messiah—both things in heaven and things on earth, all in Him. In Him we also were chosen, predestined according to His plan. He keeps working out all things according to the purpose of His will— so that we, who were first to put our hope in Messiah, might be for His glorious praise.

After you heard the message of truth— the Good News of your salvation—and when you put your trust in Him, you were sealed with the promised *Ruach ha-Kodesh*. He is the guarantee of our inheritance, until the redemption of His possession—to His glorious praise!

Ephesians 1:3-14

We too all lived among them in the cravings of our flesh, indulging the desires of the flesh and the mind. By nature we were children of wrath, just like the others. But God was rich in mercy, because of His great love with which He loved us. Even when we were dead in our trespasses, He made us alive together with Messiah. (By grace you have been saved!)

Ephesians 2:3-5a

For by grace you have been saved through faith. And this is not from yourselves— it is the gift of God. It is not based on deeds, so that no one may boast. For we are His workmanship—created in Messiah *Yeshua* for good deeds, which God prepared beforehand so we might walk in them.

Therefore, keep in mind that once you— Gentiles in the flesh—were called "uncircumcision" by those called "circumcision" (which is performed on flesh by hand). At that time you were separate from Messiah, excluded from the commonwealth of Israel and strangers to the covenants of promise, having no hope and without God in the world. But now in Messiah *Yeshua*, you who once were far off have been brought near by the blood of the Messiah. For He is our *shalom*, the One who made the two into one and broke down the middle wall of separation.

Within His flesh He made powerless the hostility— the law code of *mitzvot* contained in regulations. He did this in order to create within Himself one new man from the two groups, making *shalom*, and to reconcile both to God in one body through the cross—by which He put the hostility to death. And He came and proclaimed *shalom* to you who were far away and *shalom* to those who were near— for through Him we both have access to the Father by the same *Ruach*. So then you are no longer strangers and foreigners, but you are fellow citizens with God's people and members of God's household.

Ephesians 2:8-19

But now in Messiah *Yeshua*, you who once were far off have been brought near by the blood of the Messiah. For He is our *shalom*, the One who made the two into one and broke down the middle wall of separation.

From Ephesians 2:13-14a TLV ©2018, image #52/54

53. God Creates His Kingdom

It seemed good to the *Ruach ha-Kodesh* and to us not to place on you any greater burden than these essentials: that you abstain from things offered to idols, from blood, from things strangled, and from sexual immorality. By keeping away from these things, you will do well. *Shalom!*"

Acts 15:28-29

Brothers and sisters, you were called to freedom—only do not let your freedom become an opportunity for the flesh, but through love serve one another. For the whole *Torah* can be summed up in a single saying: "Love your neighbor as yourself."

Galatians 5:13-14

Now the deeds of the flesh are clear: sexual immorality, impurity, indecency, idolatry, witchcraft, hostility, strife, jealousy, rage, selfish ambition, dissension, factions, envy, drunkenness, carousing, and things like these. I am warning you, just as I warned you before, that those who do such things will not inherit God's kingdom. But the fruit of the *Ruach* is love, joy, peace, patience, kindness, goodness, faithfulness, gentleness, and self-control—against such things there is no law.

Galatians 5:19-23

If we live by the *Ruach*, let us also walk by the *Ruach*.

Galatians 5:25

You have been built on the foundation made up of the emissaries and prophets, with Messiah *Yeshua* Himself being the cornerstone. In Him the whole building, being fitted together, is growing into a holy temple for the Lord. In Him, you also are being built together into God's dwelling place in the *Ruach*.

Ephesians 2:20-22

Therefore I, a prisoner for the Lord, urge you to walk in a manner worthy of the calling to which you were called— with complete humility and gentleness, with patience, putting up with one another in love, making every effort to keep the unity of the *Ruach* in the bond of *shalom*.

There is one body and one *Ruach*,

just as you also were called in one hope of your calling;

one Lord, one faith, one immersion;

one God and Father of all,

who is over all and through all and in all.

But to each one of us grace was given in keeping with the measure of Messiah's gift.

Ephesians 4:1-7

Let no harmful word come out of your mouth, but only what is beneficial for building others up according to the need, so that it gives grace to those who hear it. Do not grieve the *Ruach ha-Kodesh* of God, by whom you were sealed for the day of redemption. Get rid of all bitterness and rage and anger and quarreling and slander, along with all malice. Instead, be kind to one another, compassionate, forgiving each other just as God in Messiah also forgave you.

Ephesians 4:29-32

Therefore be imitators of God, as dearly loved children; and walk in love, just as Messiah also loved us and gave Himself up for us as an offering and sacrifice to God for a fragrant aroma.

Ephesians 5:1-2

For once you were darkness, but now in union with the Lord you are light. Walk as children of light (for the fruit of light is in all goodness and righteousness and truth), trying to learn what is pleasing to the Lord.

Ephesians 5:8-10

Blessed be the God and Father of our Lord *Yeshua* the Messiah! In His great mercy He caused us to be born again to a living hope through the resurrection of Messiah *Yeshua* from the dead. An incorruptible, undefiled, and unfading inheritance has been reserved in heaven for you. By trusting, you are being protected by God's power for a salvation ready to be revealed in the last time. You rejoice in this greatly, even though now for a little while, if necessary, you have been distressed by various trials.

These trials are so that the true metal of your faith (far more valuable than gold, which perishes though refined by fire) may come to light in praise and glory and honor at the revelation of Messiah *Yeshua*. Though you have not seen Him, you love Him. And even though you don't see Him now, you trust Him and are filled with a joy that is glorious beyond words, receiving the outcome of your faith—the salvation of your souls.

1 Peter 1:3-9

So brace your minds for action. Keep your balance. And set your hope completely on the grace that will be brought to you at the revelation of *Yeshua* the Messiah. Like obedient children, do not be shaped by the cravings you had formerly in your ignorance. Instead, just like the Holy One who called you, be holy yourselves also in everything you do. For it is written,

"*Kedoshim* you shall be, for I am *kadosh*."

If you call on Him as Father—the One who judges impartially according to each one's deeds—then live out the time of sojourning in reverent fear.

1 Peter 1:13-17

Now that you have purified your souls in obedience to the truth, leading to sincere brotherly love, love one another fervently from a pure heart.

1 Peter 1:22

As you come to Him, a living stone rejected by men but chosen by God and precious, you also, as living stones, are being built up as a spiritual house—a holy priesthood to offer up spiritual sacrifices acceptable to God through Messiah *Yeshua*. For it says in Scripture,

"Behold, I lay in Zion a stone,

a chosen, precious cornerstone.

Whoever trusts in Him

will never be put to shame."

1 Peter 2:4-6

But you are a chosen people, a royal priesthood, a holy nation, a people for God's own possession, so that you may proclaim the praises of the One who called you out of darkness into His marvelous light.

Once you were "not a people,"

but now you are "God's people."

You were shown "no mercy,"

but now you have been shown "mercy."

1 Peter 2:9-10

Above all, keep your love for one another constant, for "love covers a multitude of sins." Be hospitable one to another without grumbling. As each one has received a gift, use it to serve one another, as good stewards of the many-sided grace of God. Whoever speaks, let it be as one speaking the utterances of God. Whoever serves, let it be with the strength that God supplies. So in all things may God be glorified through Messiah *Yeshua*—all glory and power to Him forever and ever! Amen.

1 Peter 4:8-11

As you come to Him, a living stone rejected by men but chosen by God and precious, you also, as living stones, are being built up as a spiritual house—a holy priesthood to offer up spiritual sacrifices acceptable to God through Messiah *Yeshua*.

From 1 Peter 2:4-5 TLV ©2018, image #53/54

215

54. God Lights the Way Home

But an hour is coming—it is here now—when the true worshipers will worship the Father in spirit and truth, for the Father is seeking such people as His worshipers. God is Spirit, and those who worship Him must worship in spirit and truth."

John 4:23-24

What was from the beginning, what we have heard, what we have seen with our eyes, what we have looked at and touched with our hands, concerning the Word of life— the life was revealed, and we have seen and testify and declare to you the eternal life that was with the Father and was revealed to us. What we have seen and heard we proclaim also to you, so you may have fellowship with us. Indeed, our fellowship is with the Father and His Son, *Yeshua* the Messiah. These things we write so our joy may be full.

Now this is the message we have heard from Him and announce to you—that God is light and in Him there is no darkness at all. If we say we have fellowship with Him and keep walking in the darkness, we are lying and do not practice the truth. But if we walk in the light as He Himself is in the light, we have fellowship with one another and the blood of His Son *Yeshua* purifies us from all sin.

If we say we have no sin, we are deceiving ourselves and the truth is not in us. If we confess our sins, He is faithful and righteous to forgive our sins and purify us from all unrighteousness.

1 John 1:1-9

Everyone who believes that *Yeshua* is the Messiah is born of God, and everyone who loves the Father loves the one born of Him.

We know that we love God's children by this—when we love God and obey His commandments. For this is the love of God—that we keep His commandments.

And His commandments are not burdensome. For everyone born of God overcomes the world. And the victory that has overcome the world is this—our faith. Who is it that overcomes the world, if not the one who believes that *Yeshua* is *Ben-Elohim*?

Messiah *Yeshua* is the One who came by water and blood—not by water only, but by water and blood. The Spirit is the One who testifies, because the Spirit is the truth. For there are three that testify— the Spirit, the water, and the blood—and these three are one.

1 John 5:1-8

"Look, He is coming with the clouds,

and every eye shall see Him,

> even those who pierced Him.

And all the tribes of the earth

> shall mourn because of Him.

Yes, amen!"

Revelation 1:7

When I saw Him, I fell at His feet like a dead man.

But He placed His right hand on me, saying, "Do not be afraid! I am the First and the Last, and the One who lives. I was dead, but look—I am alive forever and ever! Moreover, I hold the keys of death and *Sheol*.

Revelation 1:17-18

Then he carried me away in the *Ruach* to a great and high mountain, and he showed me the holy city, Jerusalem, coming down out of heaven from God, having the glory of God—her radiance like a most precious stone, like a jasper, sparkling like crystal. She had a great, high wall, with twelve gates, and above the gates twelve angels. On the gates were inscribed the names of the twelve tribes of *Bnei-Yisrael*— three gates on the east, three gates on the north, three gates on the south, and three gates on the west.

And the wall of the city had twelve foundations, and on them the twelve names of the twelve emissaries of the Lamb.

Revelation 21:10-14

I saw no temple in her, for its Temple is ADONAI *Elohei-Tzva'ot* and the Lamb. And the city has no need for the sun or the moon to shine on it, for the glory of God lights it up, and its lamp is the Lamb.

The nations shall walk by its light, and the kings of the earth bring their glory into it. Its gates shall never be shut by day, for there shall be no night there! And they shall bring into it the glory and honor of the nations. And nothing unholy shall ever enter it, nor anyone doing what is detestable or false, but only those written in the Book of Life.

Revelation 21:22-27

Then the angel showed me a river of the water of life—bright as crystal, flowing from the throne of God and of the Lamb down the middle of the city's street. On either side of the river was a tree of life, bearing twelve kinds of fruit, yielding its fruit each month; and the leaves of the tree were for the healing of the nations. No longer will there be any curse.

The throne of God and of the Lamb shall be in the city, and His servants shall serve Him. They shall see His face, and His name shall be on their foreheads. Night shall be no more, and people will have no need for lamplight or sunlight—for ADONAI *Elohim* will shine on them. And they shall reign forever and ever!

Revelation 22:1-5

Behold, I am coming soon, and My reward is with Me, to pay back each one according to his deeds.

"I am the Alpha and the Omega, the First and the Last, the Beginning and the End. How fortunate are those who wash their robes, so that they may have the right to the Tree of Life and may enter through the gates into the city.

Revelation 22:12-14

I, *Yeshua*, have sent My angel to testify these things to you for My communities. I am the Root and the Offspring of David, the Bright and Morning Star."

The *Ruach* and the bride say, "Come!" And let the one who hears say, "Come!"

Let the one who is thirsty come—let the one who wishes freely take the water of life! I testify to everyone who hears the words of the prophecy of this book. If anyone adds to them, God shall add to him the plagues that are written in this book; and if anyone takes away from the words of the book of this prophecy, God shall take away his share in the Tree of Life and the Holy City, which are written in this book.

The One giving testimony to these things says, "Yes! I am coming soon!" Amen! Come, Lord *Yeshua*! May the grace of the Lord *Yeshua* be with all!

Revelation 22:16-21

And the city has no need for the sun or the moon to shine on it, for the glory of God lights it up, and its lamp is the Lamb.
From Revelation 21:23 TLV ©2018, image #54/54

Make Your Own TLV Art Scroll!

How to color and craft your own scroll:

1) Read the stories about how God cares for us in your Grow-with-Me Bible. Tear the coloring pages out of your Grow-with-Me Bible along the perforated edges as you read each story.

2) Color the pictures with crayons, markers, or coloring pencils. You can color all the way to the edge of the paper or just highlight them with color. Color them all the same way or make them all different. Make them uniquely your own!

3) As you color each picture, use tape to attach your latest masterpiece to the one before. For best results, tape all the way down the edges of both sides of the pictures.

4) Keep your colored pages in a safe place. When you finish coloring all the pages, you should have a long scroll of pictures to remind you of all the stories you read about God and how He takes care of us!

5) Using two thin dowel rods and more tape, affix the beginning edge of the first picture to one dowel rod and the ending edge of the last picture to the second rod. Be sure to leave some of the rod sticking out above and below the page.

6) Roll both rods towards each other so that the pictures wrap around the rods with the colored pages on the inside and the back of the pages visible along the rods. The rods should meet in the middle of the line of pictures to 'close' the scroll.

7) Now you can use ribbon or string or braided yarn to tie the scroll so it doesn't unroll. You can also make a cover for it with a piece of cloth which you can decorate with cloth paint or embroidery. Then you can wrap it around the scroll to protect it before you tie it closed with the ribbon.

8) You can also decorate the tops and/or bottoms of the dowel rods. You could make little gold crowns for the tops of the rods and tie ribbons on the bottoms.

COMING SOON IN 2021...

Tree of Life Children's Bible

This 9x6 Bible will come fully illustrated with full color artwork from the Grow-with-Me Bible and lots of extra helps for kids!

Our Goal is to provide this Bible for free to children everywhere!

Visit www.tlvbiblesociety.org to give and learn more.

TLV BIBLE JOURNEY APP

Enjoy all kinds of Multimedia Bible engagement content updated weekly!

Scan to download